· *Till Break of Day* ·

December 1996

MARINA CANTACUZINO

Till Break of Day

Meeting the Challenge of HIV and AIDS
at London Lighthouse

HEINEMANN : LONDON

William Heinemann Ltd
Michelin House, 81 Fulham Road, London SW3 6RB
LONDON   MELBOURNE   AUCKLAND   TORONTO

First published 1993
Copyright © Marina Cantacuzino 1993

The author has asserted her moral rights

A CIP catalogue record for this book
is held by the British Library
ISBN 0 434 10806 5

Phototypeset by CentraCet, Cambridge
Printed and bound in Great Britain by
Butler & Tanner Ltd, Frome and London

· *Till Break of Day* ·

· One ·

It was the candle on reception that I noticed first and which made the greatest impression on me: this small twenty-four-hour cemetery candle placed at one end of the desk was a potent indicator that this was no ordinary office or organisation.

As one person after another came up to the desk wanting to know who had died, it soon became obvious to me what exactly the candle signified. They were told that the candle was for Graham who had died on the residential unit the previous night. Most people had not known Graham but those who had looked sad and one woman was visibly shocked: 'But that's terrible,' she said, 'the last time I saw him he seemed so much better.' Though Graham was known to only a few staff and volunteers, his death – like the death of anyone who used the services at London Lighthouse – sent a ripple of empathy through the building. It set a sober mood – though not a forbidding one – and made everyone think of Graham that day whether they had known him or not.

This candle was nothing more than a simple symbolic gesture but it brought home to me the proximity of death and, as I sat behind the reception desk on my first day as a volunteer at London Lighthouse, I thought a lot about

Graham even though I had never met him. The candle, representing as it did the life of someone who had died of AIDS, dislodged any previous notion I may have had about death belonging elsewhere or being confined to another part of this impressive and imposing building.

On average a candle was lit every ten days alerting everyone to the fact that someone had died, although during the course of my time as a volunteer I saw as many as three candles at any one time. There was also a candle which burned continually in the Quiet Room (a room similar to a chapel but without the religious connotations, where people could go to pray or reflect). The candle in the Quiet Room was lit in memory of all those who had died of AIDS and burned as a light of hope for people with HIV.

Another candle burnt at the nurses' station on the residential unit which was situated at the top of the building on the second floor and, in a similar way to the candle on the ground floor, conveyed the message that someone had died. It was important for other residents to be sensitive to the fact that bereaved friends and relatives might be on the unit.

Originally the idea of London Lighthouse founder Christopher Spence, the candle on the reception desk was objected to by some people because they thought it was too morbid and that it upset the calm atmosphere of the building. Spence, however, believed that lighting a candle emphasised symbolically that people, and the issue, mattered: 'People continue to be thought about well after they have died and their death is a significant event for the whole organisation.'

My first thoughts as I walked through the door of 111–117 Lancaster Road on a cold Monday morning in February were that, despite its infancy and despite its association with a modern contagious disease, London Lighthouse was a place with a past. This might have been because the original structure of the building was built in 1929 and so, contrary to its modern appearance, gave a sense that a great deal had gone on here. But more probably it was, I suspect, because within its five years' existence, London Lighthouse had burgeoned, flourished and developed beyond any of its founder members' wildest expectations, with just under 2000 people coming through reception each week to use the wide range of services now on offer.

However in 1981 this large building in Lancaster Road was just a derelict school. That year Christopher Spence and his then partner, the Reverend Andrew Henderson, moved into a house opposite and converted the basement into a counselling centre set up to look at issues related to death, dying, bereavement and disability.

At the time Spence was teaching on a diploma counselling course as well as attempting to get Cruse (the National Organisation for the Bereaved) off the ground in the Kensington and Chelsea area, while Andrew Henderson, alongside his pastoral duties, was employed as the Director of Social Services for the Royal Borough of Kensington and Chelsea.

By the summer of 1983 both Spence and Henderson, in their respective lines of work, had begun to notice disturbing signs that AIDS was not just an American disease but was fast emerging as an important local issue. Spence decided to start a support group for gay men whose lives were affected by the virus.

'At first I did not particularly want to take HIV and AIDS on as my issue,' Spence told me. 'Like a lot of people I was in a fair level of denial at the time and didn't want to face it, but then a great friend rang up one day and insisted that he had to see me immediately. When he arrived I had no idea what he was going to say but then he came out with it: "I think I've got AIDS and I'm going to die," he said, "I don't want to spin it out but I want your support." The way Frank had found out he was infected was that he'd had a relationship with a man who had died of AIDS and whose death had been blazened across the tabloid press. He wasn't well and had put two and two together.'

Frank died a short while later in the intensive care unit of an acute hospital, having had to endure the dehumanising effect of the then ill-informed and ill-equipped health service. Spence has frequently spoken of his friend, whose enforced isolation and experience of 'barrier' nursing (requiring everyone who comes in contact with the patient to wear hats, masks, gowns, aprons, gloves and even galoshes) propelled him into the frontline of the AIDS debate. 'It was Frank who first made me seriously think about taking on this issue because I made a sort of unspoken promise to him that other people wouldn't have to suffer in the way that he had.' Having seen his friend die in such clinical and oppressive surroundings, Spence was alerted to the fact that there was a desperate need for a model of care which would provide an attractive, unintimidating and loving environment.

Frank's death gave Spence a new perspective on the disease which was later to influence London Lighthouse's radical philosophy of care. In 'AIDS: An Issue for Everyone', Spence wrote of his friend: 'Among his many parting gifts was a great deal of information about the disease (and the most important realisation that it is just a disease which, like every other disease, can be fought); fresh insights into the ways in which self-hatred and deprecation, in Frank's case as a working-class gay man, is the most formidable enemy in the fight against the disease; the opportunity to be very powerful in the face of blatant prejudice and mistreatment, both of gay men and of that often forgotten sub-group of people with disabilities, the dying; and the chance to grow myself every step of the way.' Having described Frank's grief at his mother's early death, his subsequent wish to die, and his struggle to recognise his own self-worth, Spence goes on to say: 'I believe it was these three areas of deep-seated hurt, the loss of his mum and his worthless self image as a working-class gay man that made Frank so vulnerable to AIDS and unable to combat the disease in a powerful way.'

In the same week that Frank died, Jonathan Grimshaw – who was later to become director of the Landmark, the day centre for people with HIV in South London – rang Spence to tell him that he had the HTLV 3 virus (as it was then known) and was starting up a self-help group called Body Positive. He said there was an acute shortage of leaders to help set up an urgently needed support system and he asked Spence to run a course in leadership development.

Spence had also begun to develop a working partnership with John Shine, who at the time was employed as a nurse in the AIDS wing at St Stephen's Hospital and who had gone on one of Spence's bereavement counselling courses. Shine's work had made him acutely aware of the gross lack of terminal care available on the NHS and of the fact that hospices were not yet ready or willing to take in those who were dying of AIDS.

Simultaneously important links were formed with two well-known AIDS specialists, Dr Charles Farthing and Dr Tony Pinching, and as a result Spence was invited by hospitals to do workshops with their staff on death, dying and bereavement. Treatment teams tended to be young and were in the uniquely distressing position of having to confront a great many deaths amongst mostly young male patients. Hence the credibility and reputation of London Lighthouse began to be built before the building or organisation ever existed.

The prototype for Lighthouse came from an idea that Andrew Henderson and Christopher Spence had developed some years before whilst planning a community-based centre which they called the Notting Hill Centre for Life and Death. What people living with HIV and AIDS were now saying about their own experience simply pointed up the relevance of this idea and suddenly made it a real and viable proposition.

As the idea for an integrated model of care for people with HIV and AIDS began to take shape, a small group convened in Spence's and Henderson's house on Lancaster Road to discuss how such a project could be achieved. The group consisted of John Shine (later to become founder of the Red Admiral Project), Debbie Evans (of Riverside Health Authority), John Fitzpatrick (deputy director of the Terrence Higgins Trust), Peter Randall (co-founder of Body Positive who later died), Andrew Henderson and Christopher Spence. Eventually a model for a centre was formulated which would offer a range of integrated services relevant to people's disparate and changing needs. These included: a social centre, crisis intervention, one-to-one counselling, a range of training and health programmes, a home support service and a residential unit which would provide convalescent, respite and terminal care. Above all it was to provide a training and education function which was to be the key factor to changing attitudes within society as a whole.

Spence then went around the statutory sector trying to find funders. Although most people agreed such a centre was urgently needed, they could not grasp the concept of an 'integrated' model of care and simply described how it should be approached within their own particular professional frameworks. Spence soon realised he was wasting his breath as no one seemed prepared to cross boundaries between the different disciplines:

'I could see it was going to take for ever so I went back to the group and told them that I thought we were going about this all the wrong way and that the first thing we needed to do was to find a building. No one disagreed but because it seemed such a big idea, they all went away feeling very discouraged. Later that evening, I was alone in my study staring out of the window and thinking about where on earth we were going to find a suitably large building with only £750 in the bank when all of a sudden my eyes fell upon the derelict school opposite and instantly I knew that here was our building. I was so sure about it that the next day I told everybody that I'd found our building. They all looked at me as if I'd gone mad.'

Andrew Henderson, like others in the group, was not initially enthusiastic about the old school, believing it to be a formidable and depressing building, but none the less he agreed to try and trace its owners.

Up until then Spence had fought against the idea of becoming too personally involved in the project. 'I was in a relationship with Nancy Kline who lived in the United States and with whom I was also collaborating professionally, so I was spending several months of the year abroad. I liked my design for living and didn't want to change it. But then, one day in early 1985, I was driving with Nancy down Ladbroke Grove talking about our lives and future together, when suddenly I knew I had to commit myself to the project. "I think I have to do this thing myself," I said. It was a moment of true revelation.'

Spence later came to understand how his whole life had inexorably led towards this one point. 'At the age of seven I had a very clear sense of what I wanted to do with my life and Lighthouse is a very consistent expression of that,' he told me. 'But although I know I have been essential and instrumental in bringing Lighthouse about, paradoxically I also know that the project has always had a strong momentum of its own and that it was important that I should not get in the way of this.'

HIV and AIDS provided an opportunity for Spence to focus a long-standing interest in social change, liberation and the issues of health care, death, dying and loss, on a single issue which encompassed so many other issues and which had made such an impact on the lives of both himself and his friends. 'I knew that the issues confronting people living with HIV and AIDS and the source of the mistreatment, discrimination and prejudice that they experienced, had always been in society and in a way AIDS provided a spotlight to show up what was already there,' he said. 'Therefore to provide services that empowered people living with HIV and AIDS to make the best of their lives had to be only part of what we did and in a way the important thing was to change the attitude which led to this marginalisation and oppression. My path for that has always been through education and training, rather than through service providing.'

As time went by the urgent need for services became more and more apparent. Predictions based on American experience anticipated that soon the NHS would be totally overwhelmed with AIDS cases. Projected figures put forward by the Communicable Diseases Surveillance Centre, for example, estimated that by 1988 there would be 3210 people diagnosed as having AIDS in the UK of whom possibly over 2000 would be in need of medical care and support. In addition it was believed that at least 30,000 people already had the Human Immunodeficiency Virus. Later Government estimates put the figure at 40,000 with some specialists claiming that 100,000 was a more realistic figure. Against the national figures, London emerged as having the highest proportion of people living with AIDS in the country and by the end of 1986 77.5 per cent of the total number of people diagnosed were either living in or had been treated by one of the four London Regional Health Authorities, with North West Thames seeing 64 per cent of these. The acute hospital wards were reporting that costly acute beds needed for people with AIDS requiring active medical treatment were being taken up by those who did not need to be hospitalised but were in need of some kind of nursing care and support. In the voluntary sector the pioneering Terrence Higgins Trust and Body Positive were trying to extend their information and support services despite a serious lack of funding.

If the message from America was to be believed, then the implications for people living with HIV and AIDS and their carers were appalling. It was estimated that within four years existing medical provision would be totally inadequate and people with HIV and AIDS would be living in isolation, with no appropriate medical care nor a sufficient support system. In reality, the number of people to be diagnosed with AIDS was not nearly as high as had at first been predicted. But in order to understand how a place like London Lighthouse could be built and funded against a backdrop of such fear and blatant gay oppression, it is essential to remember the enormous sense of urgency that existed at that time.

The town hall rates department was unable to identify the owners of the derelict school building on Lancaster Road; they could confirm only that the rates were collected and paid on time. The only course of action left to Spence and his team was to push a letter under the door requesting that the owners of the building identify themselves. As a result, three weeks later, a letter came back from the Spanish Embassy who, it transpired, owned this derelict school. They had intended to convert it into a community centre but had run out of cash and used it instead to store surplus madonnas. The Embassy was interested in selling it for £400,000 which at the time seemed reasonable despite possible problems over planning permission.

In June 1986 the likelihood of buying this building increased when a meeting with the trustees of the John Paul Getty Junior Charitable Trust secured the Trust's agreement that, in principal, they would buy the building for the group with an interest-free loan.

It was a very exciting moment since the loan would make possible the purchase of the building after which Spence felt certain they would be able to raise the money to pay it back. However, they soon faced their first major obstacle, when the authorities in Madrid produced another bidder at the eleventh hour and within weeks the price had doubled. The trustees for John Paul Getty Junior drew the line at an interest free loan of £700,000 for two years but fortunately a further £50,000 was given by the Getty Trust and by the Delamere Trust, for which Henderson was a trustee, and the building was duly purchased on 5 August 1986.

On the same day the charity London Lighthouse was formed and its aims formally laid out in the legal document, amongst them: 'to establish homes, hospitals, services and places of resort and refuge in order to give help, medical attention and nursing to those suffering from or affected by the diseases or conditions known as or apparently related to AIDS', and, 'to encourage right-thinking attitudes to mental and physical health among such people and to alleviate deprivation, distress, isolation and despair deriving from such diseases or conditions'. No one was exactly sure who thought of the name London Lighthouse but it was a powerful image not only in the sense of lighting a passage home but also in the sense of being a pilot light for other similar schemes. Not least, the image suggested spotlighting better attitudes to HIV and AIDS (and therefore towards improved policy and provision) as well as resident/patient-centred care. The word hospice was never liked because, as Spence said, London Lighthouse was to 'provide a continuum of care, guiding people safely home (to themselves and one another) and as a source of strength and stability in stormy waters'.

Although on technical grounds Spence had been told that there wouldn't be any problem applying for planning permission, in reality AIDS was such an emotive issue that anything could happen. Before an application for change of use could be put to the planning committee, the plans had to be deposited at a local access point. The one nearest to Lancaster Road was round the corner next to Ladbroke Grove tube station and it was here that the local press learnt of the intended use of the Solomon Wolfson School. With just a few months to go before the Government launched its first AIDS information and television advertising initiative, the public were to a great extent misinformed about AIDS and when word got round the local community there was an immediate outcry.

The two main objections seemed to be, firstly, that house prices would fall because Lighthouse would be importing yet more marginal people into an area which for some time had been seen as a dumping ground for down-and-outs, with a drugs unit, a drink rehabilitation centre and two DHSS hostels already there. And secondly children's health and safety would be at risk from dirty needles found lying in the street.

Consequently an unholy alliance was formed between those who were interested in maintaining the value of their property and the parents of the children at the neighbouring primary school – most of whom lived on the estate at the end of the road. An anonymous letter featuring a skull and cross-bones was sent to houses throughout the district urging people to write and object. One of these leaflets was pinned to Spence's own front door with the words 'AIDS Deathhouse' printed in bold red letters underneath.

In addition a group of residents started lobbying local councillors and sent a petition with 800 names to the local authority demanding that the 'hospice' plan be rejected. One of the leaders of the opposition group publicly declared: 'I don't mind people who get AIDS through a blood transfusion being treated, but I'm not sorry for drug addicts and homosexuals who get it.' Shops, too, openly displayed their hostility and even a nearby flower shop protested at the idea of having such disreputable neighbours despite the obvious profit they stood to make.

Andrew Henderson, like the others in the group, had not expected such a hostile reaction: 'We'd anticipated some opposition but were surprised by the amount we got and by the sheer ferocity of people. We were even more surprised when the national press took it on as a big story because we'd only ever considered ourselves to be a little basement project. We all shared some ignorance about AIDS compared with now and there was fear on both sides. We hadn't planned an education campaign but it soon became evident that such a campaign was urgently needed and the local churches mobilised in our support and started teaching their congregations the facts about HIV.'

In the summer of 1986 a 400-strong public meeting was held at St Andrew's Methodist church at the end of Lancaster Road. Present were Dr Tony Pinching from St Mary's, Tony Whitehead and a local vicar, the Reverend Richard Adfield who courageously agreed to take the chair. The meeting was loud and angry and erupted in bitter recrimination. With feelings running high and shouts from the floor of 'keep the poofters away from here', the majority of those who attended had plainly come to heckle rather than to hear what was being said. When a woman spoke in favour of the project, one angry opponent yelled: 'I hope you get AIDS, you old cow!' Even some of those speaking in support of the project demonstrated a degree of ignorance and prejudice. For instance, one local councillor sought to reassure opponents that the high walls and relative seclusion of the site would shield them from the offending sight of those who were ill.

John Shine remembered, 'Most of the objectors in the hall were working-class but were being whipped up into a fervour by an upper-class woman who stood at the rear. She stood back and gave them the bullets to fire. Although very little was heard, it was an extremely productive meeting because it gave people the opportunity to vent their anger. But it was also pretty scary and most of us left feeling rather afraid in case we were lynched outside.'

However it was the words of two women in particular which most people remembered. The first stood up and emotionally described how she had come to London fifty years ago on the last children's train out of Czechoslovakia where there had been another killer on the rampage – this one called Hitler. She said that people in England had opened their doors to her and she couldn't understand how it was possible that people who had extended such a welcome to her could now be denying it to their own. She hoped that people would never have to feel ashamed as those who had refused to help in the past had done. After she spoke the room was filled with a pregnant hush but then all of a sudden the silence was broken as a youth leapt to his feet shouting '*Heil* Hitler'. Later, after a lot of wild talk about the unsavoury sexual practices of homosexuals, the second woman stood up and said that she had a fifteen-year-old son and a sixteen-year-old daughter and, while her son had never been harassed by gay men visiting the area, she and her daughter were constantly being harassed by heterosexual men.

Spence spoke to the gathering explaining, in his view, the meaning and implications of such overt animosity: 'If things in the community are not right for any group then they are not, in fact, right for any of us,' he said. 'It is easy to get lost in protecting our own particular interest in such a complex and diverse community but, long term, if things are not right for people affected by AIDS – and at this point they are far from right – then they are not right for any of us.' The line he took was that people's fears were understandable, even if they were not well-founded. He wouldn't permit any lashing back but instead insisted on dialogue, and part of that dialogue was listening to what was being said. 'What happened at that meeting,' he later remarked, 'had nothing to do with Lighthouse or AIDS but to do with pent-up feelings in the community about poverty and being marginalised.'

Support for the project, however, was growing daily. Press reports describing this hostile reaction fuelled people's emotions, this time in favour of the scheme. Although a television discussion programme managed to produce a bank of opponents hurling insults at a single Lighthouse representative, this naked display of ignorance and prejudice served only to create a groundswell of support. Also the public meeting seemed to have quelled community fears and, without any organised lobbying, opponents of the project started to fall away. At the same time supporters had collected a counter-petition signed by 3600 people, the biggest petition in the history of the borough. 'It was extraordinary,' said Henderson, 'how such a ferocious anti-reaction just evaporated. Some time later we held a meeting for school parents to see whether there was still fear and opposition among them and only five people turned up.'

The planning application was heard by Kensington and Chelsea's town planning committee on 9 September and received all-party approval. The chairman, Councillor Simon Orr-Ewing, said: 'We are a compassionate and responsible local authority, but for us this has probably been one of the most difficult decisions the town planning committee has ever made.'

The next stage was to invite several architects to submit plans for the site. The architects were then asked to attend a meeting in which all plans were submitted for consideration. It was a process of elimination. Four out of the five tenders hoped to impress by producing very developed projects. One plan resembled the aviary at London Zoo, while another showed rigid rows of beds along the lines of an old-fashioned NHS ward. And one architect, dressed like an undertaker, adopted a finger-wagging approach warning these 'young people' that strict rules needed to be applied. Robert Sproson, of First Architecture, was the only architect who did not bring any drawings. He explained that he couldn't produce plans without first embarking on a consultation exercise with the client.

'I went in with nothing', he recalled, 'because in my previous job, which was mainly concerned with local architecture, decisions were always made through consultation with the community. I said to Christopher Spence and the others "I don't know you and I don't know anything about care for people with AIDS, so how can I put in a proposal unless we go through a learning process together?" I didn't have any credibility as a partner in a firm of architects but because Lighthouse was then so unbureaucratic and because there was such a sense of urgency about getting the project up and running, we were given the job.'

At the same time fund raising had started in earnest and in the autumn of 1986 Spence and Henderson attended a meeting held at the Department of Health to discuss Government funding. 'We went along with the idea that the capital project would cost £2 million and we had decided we needed the Government to give us £1 million,' said Spence. 'There came a point in the meeting when the question of figures came up. We put forward our figure and then the Department of Health put forward their figure but there was this huge gap: it turned out that the Government were thinking of giving us only £10,000. Although we knew we would get something, nothing was agreed at that meeting and we still hadn't heard by June of the following year. But luckily for us that summer Mrs Thatcher called a General Election which prompted me to ring up the Department of Health to tell them that unless I knew how much they would give us I'd have to call a halt to the building programme and if that was the case it wouldn't look very good for a government hoping to be re-elected. At this point, and without hesitation, they agreed to give us the £1 million that we so urgently needed.'

By December 1986, architects, surveyors and cost-consultants had been appointed, and the Director (Christopher Spence), Counsellor (John Shine), Fund Raising Manager (Mary Pipes) and Finance and Administration Manager (Nichola Sage) were in post. The Community Services Manager, Geoff Hopping, joined the team in February 1987 and a further two staff were appointed during the year. A feature of these early days was the immense energy and total conviction people had that London Lighthouse could and would be built. Caspar Thomson who worked as a volunteer on the project before being appointed as staff said: 'It was like diving into the deep end of a pool. We had embarked on a very ambitious project without any money and quite unexpectedly we found ourselves part of a huge local uproar and in the forefront of media attention. Luckily we had a healthy naivety about the way things occurred and weren't bogged down by years of bureaucratic experience. In a miraculous sort of way things kept falling into our lap and Lighthouse began to take shape.'

Mary Pipes was one of the most inspirational appointments at that time because she brought with her some badly needed public relations and fund raising skills. Her greatest achievement was in packaging the project to make it into a fund-raising proposition. Although the early fund raising had been successfully carried out by both Spence and Henderson, she was able to attract a great deal of money by finding the right balance between presenting Lighthouse as a very successful project, while at the same time showing it to be run by a small group of beleagured pioneers who were desperately in need of cash. With her help Lighthouse raised £2 million in less than a year and went on to raise a further £5 million.

The approach adopted by First Architecture, under

the leadership of Robert Sproson and assisted by David Barrable, was an innovative one. They compiled a questionnaire and held a series of group discussions in order to find out what sort of building was actually required. People with HIV and AIDS played a major role in the survey together with doctors, nurses, social workers, occupational therapists and voluntary workers. From this work it became clear that the key thing people wanted was a place of safety which was welcoming and restful at the same time as being accessible and functional. In architectural terms this meant transforming a very austere school building into one which was completely non-institutional.

April 1987 saw the appointment of the building contractor Wiltshire Construction Ltd and work began on site to extend, adapt and equip 111–117 Lancaster Road. For the next twelve months the core staff together with fifty volunteers worked from two PortaKabins on site and began to develop London Lighthouse's range of services. While some people were planning future services, for others the work had already begun: within months the organisation was providing counselling for at least eighty people a week as well as running residential workshops in the UK and abroad.

However, by the following December, when the building was only half completed, Lighthouse faced the possibility of having to call a halt to its building programme due to lack of funds. Potentially this was a major financial crisis as it would cost an additional quarter of a million pounds just to stop and start work. Despite promises of a substantial amount of money from the Government and other charitable trusts, payment for building work was needed urgently. At this point the actor Ian McKellen, hearing that the project was in jeopardy, stepped in to save the day. He had just returned from touring his internationally acclaimed one-man show *Acting Shakespeare* in America and was confident it would find an audience in the UK. *Acting Shakespeare* managed to raise £400,000 while the rest was collected by McKellen and Lighthouse workers as they walked down the aisles rattling buckets. Marks & Spencer donated champagne for sale in the interval and Saatchi and Saatchi provided the programme.

Cash crises were common in the early days at Lighthouse with targets continually changing but, time and time again, just as it looked as if the project had finally run out of money, someone would appear with a cheque and work would go ahead as planned. It was a remarkably hand-to-mouth and precarious existence but Lighthouse seemed blessed with incredible and unfailing good fortune. Once the residential unit had opened, a friend of Spence wrote a cheque for £48,000 to pay for a whole set of Swedish automatic beds. Only later did he himself become a resident at Lighthouse, dying there in November 1988. Ironically though he found the beds he had given rather uncomfortable as he was extremely tall and had his own bed brought in for him from home. Money was raised from many different sources and the fundraising team continually had to retune their sales patter depending on whom they were talking to – be it Government officials, charitable trusts or gay leather clubs.

Many of those who were with the project from the outset remember the eighteen months spent on site with a certain amount of nostalgia: it was a unique time of dedication and single-minded determination to raise enough money to get London Lighthouse into shape. Practically everybody worked twelve hours a day, seven days a week. Sheila, an early volunteer who was later to become an employee, remembered doing everything from mending the leaking portable lavatories to showing local dignitaries round the site. 'Everything was dirty and covered in half an inch of dust. We were in three Porta-Kabins stuck on top of each other which would rock in the wind.'

On the whole the two work groups – builders and volunteers – looked upon each other with tolerance, mutual respect and mutual interest. Sometimes, however, both sides needed keeping in check. On one occasion when a group of smart, wealthy women were being shown round the building site, the builders – as builders will – began to wolf-whistle. For the public image of Lighthouse this was totally unacceptable so when the visitors had left, the foreman was asked to tell his work-force to refrain in future from harassing innocent on-lookers. At this the foreman replied: 'I'll only tell my men to stop whistling at women if you tell your men to stop oggling at my men.'

As London Lighthouse grew and began to attract more attention, jealousies and misinformation about the project inevitably started to develop. A lot of people had their own opinion as to how the project should be run and when it became apparent that their vision was not necess-arily going to be realised they became disillusioned. As with any close-knit group of people fighting for some-thing they passionately believed in, strong attachments and loyalties had been formed and, with the expansion of the project bringing in new and trained workers, some people who had been working for Lighthouse from the earliest days felt left out in the cold.

Misinformation was abundant, partly because the AIDS field was rife with gossip but also because Lighthouse was already attracting jealousy from other care institutions.

For example, word got round that London Lighthouse would only accept someone for terminal care if, on admission, that person agreed to leave their money to the project. The reality was that London Lighthouse, like all charities, had a legacies leaflet which gave people a choice to leave their money to the project if they so wished. Another rumour suggested that Lighthouse planned to display corpses in glass coffins in the reception area – this piece of misinformation came about because of plans to have a viewing room for the dead, which was common practice in most hospitals and hospices. Sometimes the public's interest seemed excessively morbid. When two elderly local residents came to look at the site and saw a great hole dug in the ground for the lift shaft, one was overheard saying to the other: 'You see, I told you they'd dig a big hole for all the corpses.'

Training was undertaken in the local community to educate people about AIDS. Barclays Bank at the end of the road, which Lighthouse wanted to handle their account, needed a one-day induction course because some members of staff had been worried about contagion due to handling the money of people with AIDS.

Having moved their offices on site to supervise the building process, the architects soon began to feel as enthusiastic and passionate about the project as those who had been involved since the beginning. Both Sproson and Barrable got more involved with the client body than is normal for architects, working a seven-day week and finding it difficult to disentangle themselves from the new world they had suddenly entered. Sproson even attended Spence's weekend residential course on 'Life, Death and the Challenge of AIDS', an action he considered essential to understanding his client's needs.

Once people could see that the building was nearing

completion and that Lighthouse was employing more and more staff with nowhere to put them, the pressure on the architects to have the building finished intensified. In the summer of 1988 the first nurses were employed in order to develop policies for the residential unit. One volunteer remembered their arrival as a very significant moment: 'It was terribly exciting because suddenly it felt as if what we'd all been working towards for the past two years was actually going to happen. These nurses were young, enthusiastic doers rather than talkers.'

Although there was always a recruitment, self-selection and training procedure for volunteers at Lighthouse, as time went by this had to be developed and streamlined and inevitably sometimes people didn't project the right sort of image. Also some of the volunteers wanted to work for Lighthouse for inappropriate reasons, for instance because their partner had recently died and they needed a place to mourn, or because it was a safe and, at that time, almost exclusively gay environment.

In the end there was a phased hand-over with the first floor completed and ready for occupation at the end of July 1988. Fourteen full-time staff and twenty volunteers moved out of a variety of temporary office accommodation into the new building. 'Moving into the new offices,' said Sheila, 'was quite a shock because suddenly it felt as if Lighthouse had changed from being a family into an organisation. We lost some of the make-do-and-mend attitude which was inevitable and necessary, but also rather sad. From then on departments became a little more isolated and Lighthouse experienced the same sort of departmental disputes that existed in every other institution. In that way I'm afraid we weren't special.'

The remaining two floors were finished in September and the entire centre was ready to receive its first residents at the end of the month. To extend a 20,000 square foot derelict building by 13,000 square feet and adapt and equip it in eighteen months was no mean achievement. By the time HRH The Princess Margaret officially opened London Lighthouse on 23 November 1988, all of the services included in the original model of care were fully operational. The work of hundreds of people who had contributed to the project was recognised in a commemorative stone bearing the inscription 'Re-built by many hands for London Lighthouse, a Centre for people facing the challenge of AIDS'. The stone itself was one of two foundation stones laid when the original building was erected. One had been dedicated to the Solomon Wolfson School while the other had been left blank. 'It was,' said Christopher Spence, 'almost as if the original architects knew the building was to have a later life.'

Inevitably the building, as well as the organisation, had its critics and there were those who said they found it intimidating and overbearingly middle-class. Sproson disagreed totally with this criticism and defended his creation to the end. 'We asked people from every different sort of social background and with a wealth of different experiences to describe what was needed,' he explained. 'And what we learnt from the client group was that they wanted to have the very best that was available in terms of design and furnishings. The trouble is as soon as you start putting quality judgments on what is the best, then you're in deep water. Things that look nice tend to be expensive but I see that as a wholly positive thing, because it says that people with AIDS deserve the best. Working at Lighthouse has made me realise that it is impossible to design for everyone, you can only ever take it down to common things.'

By the time the building was officially opened, London

Lighthouse was able to embark on a recruitment and induction programme which eventually brought its staff complement up to eighty-five. Over 2500 registered their interest in working at the Centre. In September 1988 Spence wrote in the *Leading Lights* newsletter: 'Rigorous application to our equal opportunities and anti-racism policies has resulted in us appointing an increasingly diverse group of staff, more accurately reflecting the wider population and hopefully making London Lighthouse more accessible to every group affected by AIDS. Within the organisation we welcome the changes that this will bring.'

However, not everybody welcomed these changes. Many of the volunteers felt unfairly treated when they failed to be offered jobs and as a result left to continue their work elsewhere. One volunteer who remained with the project said that the dividing line between staff and volunteers became much more apparent once the building was occupied. 'Lighthouse had to be seen to be an efficient organisation run by professionals. Some of the volunteers who helped out while the building was being constructed (many of whom had struggled and come to terms with the fact that Lighthouse was never going to be exactly what they had envisaged) now felt alienated because there didn't seem to be a role for them anymore. People went around saying there was no difference between London Lighthouse and ICI.'

Spence admitted: 'There was a big sea change when we became significant employers of paid staff. The army of volunteers who had done so much work for us at the beginning felt threatened because whereas before we had still been members of a very loose network, suddenly everyone was having to work under proper terms and some people found it very hard to adapt.'

Many of those who left were members of the co-counselling community. The theory of co-counselling maintains that everyone is born loving, creative, zestful, intelligent, powerful and good but early childhood experiences hurt us and suppress these qualities. The natural way to heal ourselves is to release the emotions which accompany hurt, for instance tears for grief and shaking for fear. Young children do this naturally so that when they have stopped crying and screaming, they go about their daily business as usual. Co-counselling encourages adults to do likewise – to release pent-up feelings which become destructive – which in normal life they would be discouraged from doing. Co-counselling, as a method of self-recovery and mutual suppport, had been a very important part of the initial energy and philosophy of London Lighthouse and was certainly instrumental in turning around the individual experience of people with HIV and AIDS from a negative one to a positive one. Until it became evident that Lighthouse needed to diversify and that no single counselling approach should be used, the intention at the beginning was for this philosophy to inform the development of the whole project.

But Spence quickly realised that while the techniques of co-counselling were laudable, the cultish exclusivity and dependent behaviour which sometimes accompanied the practice was incompatible with the sort of organisation he was trying to build. 'A lot of people described us as a community and I began to worry that Lighthouse would soon become like a church, with people either belonging or not belonging. I understood that both the public as well as potential service users had a perception of Lighthouse which wasn't wholly useful to us and I knew there was something fundamentally limiting and unhealthy about this. Lighthouse needed to be accessible to everybody and we didn't want a framework which made people feel excluded. In building this project I was trying to avoid institutionalising such things and I felt it was dangerous to promote a philosophy which said that only those who subscribed to the philosophy were members of the club.

'But I never entirely abandoned the principles of co-counselling because I have always believed in the value of emotional discharge and see it as a very important process in the recovery of empowerment and in implementing change. I tried to keep in the organisation some of the things about co-counselling which were so rich and helpful to people in a way that would not endanger what we did.'

Thus by naturalising the co-counselling approach so that it was no longer a distinct technique, a few co-counselling methods had been successfully assimilated into the organisation. For instance, one very important principle, intrinsic to London Lighthouse, was the value attached to staff support. This meant that every member of staff was encouraged to spend one and a half hours a week engaged in giving attention to themselves in the way of a support group. To outsiders this may have seemed like a luxury, and at a cost of £70,000 a year in staff time perhaps even a waste of money as well, but for people working in a place which was dealing with so much loss on a daily basis, recovery and restoration were essential if burn-out and rapid staff turnover were to be avoided.

It was also routine at Lighthouse for meetings to begin and end with what were known as opening and closing circles – another co-counselling tool which was given great importance. As Spence once explained they provided: 'an opportunity for everyone present, in turn and without interruption, to speak personally in answer to questions posed by the person leading the meeting . . . Before the formal agenda is tackled, equality is established by everyone speaking, sharing non-work related experience, expressing hopes and objectives for the meeting, as well as being welcomed, acknowledged and listened to with respect . . . At the end of the meeting, a closing circle can be used to focus on people's perception of what has been accomplished in the meeting and of its particular value to them; to inspire one another's commitment to shared goals in the work; to anticipate some specific personal pleasure ahead; and, most important of all, to strike a blow against the self-doubt, which lurks in all of us, by appreciating one another.'

Although, like Spence, John Shine was aware that the technique of co-counselling could be put to misuse, he was a passionate believer in its process and committed to a method of work based on the importance of emotional discharge. For this reason he began to find himself increasingly marginalised at Lighthouse and consequently left the project shortly after it opened in 1988 in order to set up his own Red Admiral Project. But while management at Lighthouse may not have been satisfied with Shine's way of working, there is much evidence to suggest that service users were, since many left the organisation with him in order to pursue his method of counselling.

I met Shine on several occasions and was very impressed by him. In fact, of everyone I met whilst working at London Lighthouse, Shine was the person for whom I grew to have the greatest respect. He possessed great humanity combined with a rare humility. When I went to see him at the Red Admiral Project, we sat in a room carpeted with cushions and talked at length about Light-house and about his role in the project's development.

Shine believed that his working relationship with Spence had been developed and sustained through co-counselling. 'We were from very different backgrounds. He was upper-class and I was working-class and in a normal situation we would never have been talking to each other in this way,' he said. 'The vision for London Lighthouse came from inspiration, but we had to develop that vision and translate our dreams into reality. Of course, since we were in the grip of gay oppression, we kept meeting with opposition – individually and collec-tively – and in order for it not to distract or undermine us we had to use the skills of co-counselling. It gave us a vision, so that although we came up against numerous pressures, we never compromised. If we hadn't dealt with our feelings as they came up, we would never have realised our dreams. It was an extremely exciting process and because of it we became very close friends.'

It was clear when I first met Shine that he had felt intensely disappointed with Lighthouse both because he felt his views had been marginalised but also because he believed the bond between himself and Spence – a man he had come to admire and cherish – had been severed. But, although he had obviously been deeply hurt by the experience and regretted many things, remarkably he harboured no feelings of bitterness or blame. When I met him, several years after these events, he was delighted to have re-established a warm and close friendship with Spence.

The new staff intake reflected the need to expand Lighthouse's client group and workforce well beyond the world of gay men. So far the project had been initiated by a group of mainly white, middle-class, gay men and even before opening it had acquired a reputation for being selective and cliquish. But with the deliberate move to employ more women and heterosexual men, scepticism grew among the gay community.

Certainly there were some blatantly unsuitable appointments – some of whom left of their own accord while others were asked to leave. Spence saw the problem as one of keeping apace with change: 'We were having to recruit people for jobs with very vague job descriptions which would then suddenly change. For instance, there were only twelve staff at the beginning of 1988 but by the end of the year there were 100, so of course the nature of some jobs changed dramatically. There were therefore some people who had a particular contribution to make whilst setting up the project, but who then found they had no further role to play and obviously this caused difficulties. These were mostly people who didn't have a great deal of professional confidence and who lacked the skills to manage people in an organisation which was changing and expanding daily.'

Despite the fact that London Lighthouse was set up to be an unoppressive organisation looking at issues of class, racism and equal opportunities, some of the workforce began to criticise the management for behaving in a defensive and hostile manner. One member of the management team who left shortly after it opened told me: 'The forces against Lighthouse not working as a caring organisation were far, far greater than I had ever anticipated. In my naivety I really believed it could and would be all things to all people, but criticism, which is always a focus for people's negativity, came from everywhere – from the staff group as well as from outside. Much of this criticism was directed at Christopher Spence who seemed to welcome it at that stage. He listened to what was being said and didn't try to defend it. He separated out the truth from what was false and tried to deal with everything that was being said in a constructive and direct way.'

The same ex-employee described the methods then used in recruiting volunteers. 'In the early days we'd try to get out of people why they were really there, in other words what their motivation was. Usually they said that they had spare time or they wanted to do something valuable with their lives and put something back into society. But that was never the whole story – people were also curious, frightened and unsorted. I used to ask people what their hidden agenda was. If they admitted they'd come because they were lonely then I told them that was fine and we could help by putting them into a support group, but I explained that they weren't here to use people with AIDS to help them overcome their loneliness. The more vulnerable and open they were the more they got out of it. Some people didn't participate in the process and wouldn't allow anyone into their lives but for others it was a life-changing experience. You can't do it alone, you need the collective support of other people to make change and the induction courses, like the early workshops, were phenomenal.'

To move from dream to reality in only two years and to adjust to all the changes which that inevitably brought with it was clearly too much for some people to handle, and several staff left during the following year. Many of them held the view that Lighthouse had not succeeded in putting its philosophy into practice or in pioneering the radical form of care it had spoken of with such zeal. One person said: 'Lighthouse started off as a completely unique and proactive institution and ended up, just like any other institution, becoming more and more reactive and uninventive.'

Because London Lighthouse promised so much and

because its commitment to change was so seminal, it could not fail to disappoint some people along the way, particularly those who were involved in the project from the beginning and who had envisaged a very different end result. Although the aims of the founder members were broad and attempted to be all-embracing, it became clear, even before the building's official opening, that it could never hope to be all things to all people.

· *Two* ·

My connection with London Lighthouse went back as far as 1986 when I was told about plans for its development by the brother of Christopher Spence, whom I happened to be working with at the time on a drama series for Granada Television in Manchester. It struck me then as a remarkably brave and defiant undertaking and from then on I followed its progress keenly in the press. And when I returned to London a year later I found myself frequently driving past the site, intrigued by what was going on inside.

Although I thought the cause admirable, it didn't occur to me then that I would ever get involved in the project. Not because I didn't want to but because I felt unqualified to work in the field of HIV and AIDS. I also assumed it to be an exclusively gay arena and didn't imagine that a middle-class, heterosexual married woman like myself, with no prior experience of HIV or voluntary work, could possibly be the sort of person London Lighthouse would be prepared to train. Apart from this I was about to embark on a full-time job for a magazine and although I had always wanted to do some sort of community work, I knew this was not the right time.

In the winter of that year my husband and I gave a

party. Among the guests were two gay male friends, both of whom I knew felt ill at ease in predominantly hetero-sexual company. I sensed as they left that they had not enjoyed the evening and sure enough one of them admit-ted later that such gatherings were becoming increasingly distasteful to him. 'You see,' he said, 'I can't enjoy an evening like that because it all seems so trivial and unimportant. I'm used to going to parties and looking across the room and wondering if that person opposite will still be alive next year.' The statement horrified me and made me more aware than ever of the changes that the gay community were having to endure.

But it wasn't until two years later when I finally took the plunge to go freelance that I found I at last had enough space in my life to consider voluntary work. My know-ledge of London Lighthouse – although purely anecdotal – had increased, as had my knowledge of AIDS, and I knew that if I was going to work for a voluntary organis-ation it had to be one dealing with the issues of HIV. London Lighthouse seemed the most obvious choice because it was a local project situated only ten minutes from where I lived.

London Lighthouse both impressed and inspired me. I was impressed because here was a magnificent three-storey building constructed against all odds in a climate of open hostility towards gay men. Architecturally it was entirely non-institutional; in fact, with its high ceilings, glazed walkways and abundant use of natural materials, it reminded me more of a health and fitness centre or modern art gallery than of a nursing home or hospice. The Lighthouse philosophy was reflected in the bold design of the building – namely that AIDS was a fact of life that shouldn't be hidden away behind closed doors. The front door, therefore, opened straight on to the street, the exterior walls curved to embrace the world outside and the Lighthouse image was taken up in the design through an atrium and a light shaft. By making the physical surroundings so good, the architects were making a bold statement about the way people with AIDS should be treated. It denounced the popular notion that voluntary organisations should be indistinct, underground ventures and laid the way for a new philosophy in health care.

And I was inspired because for the first time in my life I knew I was about to become professionally involved in something that was hugely significant. Yet at the same time, I felt personally extremely insignificant. I'm not sure why this should be – perhaps because I did not have the virus myself and knew that there would therefore always be a wall of unshared experience separating me from those who did. For no matter how much you support, empathise and become involved with someone who has HIV, at the end of the day, because you are well, you can go home knowing that in all probability you have a future ahead of you. I knew I wouldn't be stared at on the bus, I wouldn't be discriminated against at work or turned out of the place where I lived. Nor would I lie awake at night wondering which part of my body would next be racked by some new virulent and persistent bug.

Given my feelings of insignificance, therefore, initially I felt a little afraid and very intrigued by what went on in the residential unit. During my first few weeks at London Lighthouse I only once had reason to go up to the unit and that was to deliver some flowers for a resident, but on that first visit it had seemed to me that the atmosphere was highly charged and the residents and nurses – by the very fact of being there – were all exceptional individuals. Later, when I became a volunteer on the unit and became accustomed to how it was run, it lost its mystique and I saw it rather as the homely, familiar place it was where, like in any family, a lot of love and happiness existed alongside a lot of anger and frustration. The sense of mystery I had about the unit came from the fact that this was the place where people died and, although if you worked on reception you were not part of the dying process, it nevertheless had its residual effect.

Residents were names rather than faces when you worked on reception, however, especially those who were too ill to use the cafe or to go for a wander into the garden. On my first day working as a volunteer on the reception desk a middle-aged couple arrived straight from the airport. They had flown over from America because their son had suddenly been taken seriously ill. They came to the desk and asked if they could see Ron T. Once I'd made sure that they were expected I showed them to the lift. They were warm, open people and as we walked through the drop-in centre they began to tell me how much their son meant to them although over the past ten years they hadn't seen as much of him as they would have liked to.

Then, two days later, I overheard someone say that Ron T. had left the building. I was surprised that he had been well enough to leave when his parents had been so concerned about his deteriorating health. I later learnt, however, that this person had been referring to Ron's body which the undertakers had already removed. I felt very sad when I heard this. I'd never met Ron T., indeed I'd only had a short conversation with his parents, and yet somehow that brief exchange had touched me and I felt their loss greatly.

Another time I got a call from a nurse saying that Kenyons were bringing John F. for the mezzanine. 'Kenny, who?' I asked, not understanding what on earth she was talking about. It was then explained to me that Kenyons were the undertakers and the mezzanine was where the mortuary was situated. Later, a hearse arrived and a coffin was carried through the side entrance to the lift. This side entrance was in full view of the main reception area and I was surprised that more attempt hadn't been made to conceal this very obvious image of death.

The reception drop-in area was the heart of London Lighthouse – the central point through which everyone had to arrive or leave. Only corpses were carried out by the side entrance – partly because of easy access to the carpark but also to deflect, though not to eliminate altogether, such public evidence of death. Originally, when the architects Robert Sproson and David Barrable were drawing up the plans for Lighthouse, a questionnaire had been circulated among workers and client groups, asking them, among other things, what provision should be made for the transport of bodies to and from the centre. People felt divided on the issue.

One person, writing in favour of a separate exit, said, 'I feel sure that while we should not be afraid of confronting death, those new to the counselling programmes might initially be frightened by seeing coffins and perhaps not come back. Also, mourning relatives would probably prefer privacy.' Another person expressed a desire for 'especially brightly coloured cloth to be placed over all bodies being removed from the main entrance, i.e. no denial of death or associating it with dark, depressing colours, or by slipping the coffin out the back.' A separate exit was finally adopted, though not a concealed one, so that everything that happened there was in full view of the drop-in area.

The design of the building with no back entrance for

the secret transport of corpses bore out one aspect of London Lighthouse's vision for its future: 'To work to change engrained social attitudes which collude to deny that death and dying are central facets of life and living.' Seeing the coffins come and go, witnessing weekly services and memorial services which took place in the Ian McKellen hall directly opposite the cafe and handing over death certificates for collection were all constant reminders that dying was still a central part of life at Lighthouse.

Even those who worked there but who had not yet been close to someone who had died experienced loss and sadness. Khaldun, the Head of Counselling, told me that he sensed a large number of people in the building were grieving. 'I sometimes see a subtle blanket or film of sadness which isn't fully acknowledged and which people aren't always consciously aware of. It filters down very softly when I enter the building and is often there in some degree or another. I think this is inevitable but I believe we need to get better at acknowledging it and at grieving consciously by developing more rituals and ceremonies. The candle is important but at the same time it's yet another thing to create a feeling of sadness, because even if you've never been up to the residential unit, there's a recognition that loss and death are present, and the feelings about that are played out by people being stressed, snappy, tired and fed up – all emotions which I see being related to grief.'

When Khaldun told me this, I understood and accepted what he was saying although I didn't feel it was yet part of my own personal experience. I'd been involved with Lighthouse for only a few weeks and hadn't at that point formed any close relationships. Subsequently, of course, I did and although I knew it was enormously healthy to be involved in a place like Lighthouse where death was treated naturally and unceremoniously – ceasing to be something abnormal or covert – it inevitably became more difficult and painful to deal with as I grew closer to people with HIV and AIDS. On the other hand, the more accustomed I became to people dying the less mystery it held for me. In time the candles no longer sent a shudder through my body, although they never ceased to have an abrasive effect, and the sight of a hearse reversing into the carpark no longer seemed sinister or strange.

The year after I had first heard about plans for Lighthouse from Spence's brother, I spent a brief spell working in Newcastle for Tyne Tees Television as a researcher and it was here that I met a fellow freelance researcher called Nigel Sheldrick. We never got to know each other well since I was coming to the end of a contract just as he was beginning a new one, but for a short while we occupied the same desk in an open-plan office. I remember one day he went down to London for a doctor's appointment and returned looking tense and withdrawn. I knew he was gay and the thought flickered through my mind that he might possibly be HIV positive.

I didn't think about Nigel again until three years later when, during my first visit to London Lighthouse, I saw a photo of him pinned to the noticeboard above someone's desk. It was the cover to his memorial service which I later discovered was pinned above several other people's desks as well. In a building which had born witness to so many funerals, this was a poignant reminder of the effect Nigel had had on so many people's lives. It transpired that he had been very involved in Lighthouse, having been one of the few men at the time willing to talk publicly about having AIDS. I was later to meet many people who had known him, all of whom spoke warmly of him, particularly men who had joined his support group and who said that without Nigel's help they would never have been able to come to terms with their own diagnosis.

As a tribute to him in the March 1990 edition of *Lighthouse News* Christopher Spence wrote: 'Finally we record with great sadness the death of Nigel Sheldrick, a much loved founding figure. He was a model of what it means to live well with HIV and AIDS, and he consistently reached out to help others along the way. His many media appearances on behalf of Lighthouse, in which he presented the human face of AIDS with power, tenderness and eloquence were an inspiration to us all. At his funeral I recalled the occasion, on the very day he received his diagnosis of AIDS, when I asked him what he thought I should tell the senior pupils of a large school to whom I was speaking about AIDS the next day. He looked at me intently and replied, "Just tell them that all is well in the world; tell them, everything is as it should be."'

Both before and after Nigel's death, Spence often drew on Nigel's experience to use in public talks as an illustration of someone who prepared well for death and who, in the process of getting physically weaker, grew in strength of mind and spirit. Shortly before he died Nigel wrote the following words, and when I read them I could see why Lighthouse considered him to be one of their most important envoys:

'I feel that, just possibly, physical death is a doorway to all of us realising that incredible spontaneity and potential that is continually bursting around and in us. Perhaps heaven and hell are sort of within us and we have the potential to live in heaven now – if we can go through the veil of anguish and tears we have built up over the years. If only we could really see our splendour, if only we could all see each other's splendour, what a different world it would be. My dream is that we can all put our vision of life into practice every day. I regard myself on a journey with trials and tribulations, with darkest despair, but also with hope, laughter and happiness. My hope is that those around can sit with me, and be alongside me as I struggle and grow.'

The words moved me greatly. As a practising Buddhist for nearly ten years, still struggling with the concept of the eternity of life, I found Nigel had summed up feelings I'd never been able to express or entirely come to grips with.

Nigel's attitude to death epitomised the very best of London Lighthouse's philosophy. Before I came to work at Lighthouse, I was under the impression that AIDS caused havoc in people's lives in a cruel and unforgiving way and that nothing productive could ever be salvaged from the wreckage. It seemed to be a disease of explosive, nightmarish dimensions and as such had caught my imagination in a way I saw it do with so many of my contemporaries. We were what you would call the 'worried well' and when news of the disease first emerged in the mid-eighties, it became the main topic of conversation at every party or social gathering. Some feared such conversations while others seemed to relish them; some went and got themselves tested, while others considered it unnecessary; but by and large most felt reasonably confident that they had not been targeted by this fatal contagious disease.

When I say AIDS captured my imagination, I do not mean it in a morbid or sensationalist way but simply because my whole life had, in one way or another, been a preparation for my work at Lighthouse. I did not realise this until later but subconsciously my identification with the problem of AIDS came from the fact that it was affecting so many young men and cutting them down in the prime of their life. In my own family there had been three young men – my brother and my two first cousins – all of whom had died before the age of twenty-five from the fatal muscle-wasting disease Duchenne Muscular Dystrophy. The disease affects only males and starts manifesting in terms of visible physical deterioration from about the age of seven – usually culminating in death from heart failure between the ages of eighteen and twenty-five.

Although I knew having a hereditary degenerative disease from birth was very different from being infected by the HIV virus in adulthood, none the less both forms of illness struck down young men in the first flush of youth in what seemed to me a random and reckless manner. I had hated the look of my brother's wasted and lifeless limbs and although he had never known what it was like to be fit and mobile I saw a parallel between his life and the lives of all the young men I met who had AIDS. The loss of muscle tone, suppleness and hair in people with AIDS was a cruel attack on the virility of men who cared so much about their physique and looking attractive.

I was never apprehensive about my work at Lighthouse. In fact people's reactions often surprised me. Some were intrigued, some were worried, a few appeared to be downright horrified, but almost all were full of admiration for what I was about to do. As far as they were concerned I was embarking on a heroic journey into a dangerous and frightening world. To me, however, it did not seem that way at all and although I was a little anxious about entering a new line of work in an organisation as yet completely unknown to me I was never worried about being with or working alongside people who had AIDS.

· *Three* ·

There was often a great warmth and openness in the way people related to each other at Lighthouse, which may partly have been to do with the fact that the building was occupied by so many gay men. It was not an atmosphere I ever felt uncomfortable in since even as a child many of my parents' close friends had been homosexual and long before my involvement with Lighthouse the men whose friendships I valued most almost always happened to be gay. I used to think this said more about me than it did about gay men because, having gone to an all-girls school and a single-sex college at university, I wasn't very used to men.

The male figures in my childhood (my father and brother) didn't really count – my father because he worked so hard that he was a fairly remote figure in our everyday lives, and my brother because he was so ill that his male identity eventually got taken over by his identity as a disabled person. One way or another this left me often feeling uneasy with, and unequal to, men. Many women find friendships with gay men easier because there is no sexual threat. In my experience and from what I have observed among my female friends, heterosexual men may indeed be interested in having friendships with women but more often than not that will involve only women whom they find attractive.

Even when I was at Lighthouse many people were still trying to eliminate the widely held view that it had been built exclusively for gay men, but the message was slowly getting through, helped by the fact that there was an increasing number of heterosexual male staff (12 per cent). However, there were still far more homosexual men working in the building and particularly at the volunteer level, where only 3 per cent were heterosexual. Ciaran, a Neighbourhood Team Development Officer, told me that he had been at a meeting for Lighthouse volunteers and part of the evening was an invitation to look at the hopes and fears each of them had in relation to working with people with HIV:

'I remember mine clearly,' he said. 'It was a hope that soon heterosexual men will start to take on this issue in the way that so many lesbians, gays and heterosexual women have done. It's not that I think that heterosexual men have anything unique to offer or that they will do anything better than we are already doing, but it's more a feeling of exasperation that HIV will never be seen as anything other than marginal until they get involved.'

Six months later, when I attended the 1991 London Lighthouse annual conference, I put my name down to take part in the workshop on 'heterosexual men'. Unfortunately in over 100 people, there was not one who identified as a heterosexual man and consequently the workshop consisted of five women and two gay men.

A great many women I spoke to who worked at Lighthouse felt a safety and warmth among gay men. One volunteer who was a nun told me that she had found a depth to God since coming to Lighthouse because 'God is love and there is so much love in this place.' She had begun working in the AIDS world precisely because she wanted to work with gay men. In the heterosexual world, she said, people were more contained and self-sufficient because they had their families, their wives and their husbands. Another volunteer, who was in her sixties, felt that since working at Lighthouse she'd come to know something she'd never known before – committed and loving friendships with men based on a mutual understanding and respect. 'I've been threatened by men all my life,' she said, 'and this is the first place I've felt safe enough to be myself.'

As for me, a heterosexual woman, I always felt in a minority at Lighthouse, but I never felt marginalised. Although I am sure every woman working there had at one time or another encountered staff and service users who displayed some distaste for women by being patronising or offensive, it was no more than you would find in any organisation whether predominately heterosexual or homosexual. One female member of staff told me she thought it was nonsense to think that as a woman you couldn't be harassed by gay men. She wasn't referring to insulting behaviour, but rather to the fond embraces of one particular man who engulfed her in hugs and kisses every time she met him in the corridor. His intrusive behaviour, which she had never encouraged, made her extremely uncomfortable with him.

For many gay men and women London Lighthouse was a sanctuary, providing a truly liberating atmosphere of tolerance and mutual respect, and unlike in most organisations a place where AIDS was not being used as an excuse to exercise new levels of discrimination. For some, Lighthouse provided the first working environment in which they were able to express openly their sexuality, and this meant not only identifying as a gay man or woman, but speaking and behaving freely and without censure. For Carol, Group Head of Community Services, coming to Lighthouse meant that for the first time in her life her sexuality was not an issue. 'I've always been open about my sexuality – even in my previous job as a social worker I thought it was better to be "out" rather than dragged "out", but I didn't realise how much time and energy I used to spend fighting people until I came here.'

However, the feeling of safety that people got from working in an organisation which understood the prejudices and oppression that gay people have had to endure could never be carried over into life on the other side of the wall in Lancaster Road. Caroline, a lesbian in her early twenties, felt accepted at Lighthouse from her first day at work because, like Carol, her sexuality was not an issue. At the same time she could see that being cosseted and over-protected in such a safe and supportive environment made the heterosexual world outside that much more difficult to deal with because her expectations were now so much higher.

Ciaran felt that being a gay man working at Lighthouse had other drawbacks: if you liked going to gay pubs and clubs, the chances were that you'd never be able to leave work behind you. 'People will come up to me and start talking about Lighthouse, even if it's the last thing I want to talk about,' he told me. 'Also, when gay men realise that you work there they immediately make the assumption that you must be HIV positive. I am always slow to deny anything about my status because I think the best situation is that we don't know about each other's status and don't let it become an issue. If I sleep with someone, I never ask his status because I always make sure I have safe sex. At first I had to make a conscious effort not to think about status and it felt rather artificial but now it's a learned thing and has become second nature to me.'

One of the most stressful things about his job, he said, was that it was so connected to his life. It had happened once, for instance, that a man he'd had sex with three months previously had ended up as a resident on the unit, and that the notes of a man he'd once had an affair with had landed on his desk. There had also been an occasion when he'd fallen in love with a service user for whom he'd been the key worker. Once he recognised what was happening, he changed his role and, although it was a hard thing to have to do, he handed the responsibility for that man over to another home support organiser.

Although practically all the paid members of staff who worked on reception were women, there were a number of male volunteers. Lighthouse was trying to get away from the female-only image of reception staff, while at the same time showing publicly as you enter the building that it was not an organisation run by and for gay men. At any one time there was always a member of staff and a volunteer manning the desk, except between 10 p.m. and 7 a.m. when the night caretaker assumed duty. The revised job description 'centre support worker' was an attempt to get away from the stereotyped passive image that most people had of receptionists. As a volunteer on the reception desk I never at any one point felt I was less valuable or had less say than a paid member of staff. Here, though not everywhere in the building, I felt that volunteers had parity with paid members of staff. The goal of parity between paid and unpaid workers (in all terms and conditions of service except pay) was, I soon learnt, an unusual and key component in the organisation's success.

Several volunteers who had worked both at reception

and on the residential unit told me they found working on reception more stressful than the unit because there was the constant feeling that anything could happen here and that it was your ultimate responsibility. Although there was also this feeling on the residential unit, a team of nurses existed to shield you from that final responsibility. Also, to a certain extent, you could feel cornered on reception. You had to keep to your post and in doing so some service users came to view you as a friendly and familiar face always available for a chat. Needless to say, certain volunteers and members of staff had what appeared to be friendlier faces than others and were consequently in greater demand. There were two volunteers at Lighthouse – both women – who whenever I saw them would be bent double in consultation with some person or other.

Meg – a woman who had spent all her adult life devoted to raising her three children and who had never known a gay man in her life before responding to an appeal for Lighthouse volunteers on television – was the sort of woman who liked to mother everyone, and there were certain service users who made sure they came into the building only when she was on duty. On several occasions I had to abandon a lunch engagement with her because there was someone else far more needy of her time than I.

For instance, once she spent hours trying to coax a seventeen-year-old girl who'd just arrived from Ireland to eat some lunch. On discovering that she was HIV-positive, the girl had run away from her Catholic parents because she knew she would never be able to bear their shame and sense of blame. She had arrived in London and come straight to Lighthouse where she had locked herself inside the Quiet Room. Meg sat outside the room with a tray of food urging her to come out and eat as nothing had passed her lips for forty-eight hours. Although she was no longer officially on duty, Meg didn't leave the building until the girl emerged three hours later.

Similarly Jane who came to Lighthouse when it was still operating from PortaKabins had infinite patience and time for people. Her involvement with Lighthouse began almost by accident. She lived locally and had one day passed by the building site when something told her to stop and peer through the gates. 'Instinct told me that this was going to be a very important place,' she said. For me, and for many others, Jane epitomised the London Light-house spirit of non-judgemental care and support.

It had been Jane who had been working on the desk the day that Sam walked through the double doors. Sam was to become my greatest friend and ally at Lighthouse and although he was a very prominent figure in the organis-ation he always seemed to maintain a healthy balance between his work there as a volunteer and his life outside. He was sure that it was Jane's welcome that had made him persist in coming to Lighthouse and offer his services as a volunteer. He had felt so vulnerable at the time that the slightest wrong move would have sent him running. He once said to me: 'The person who's on duty as you enter Lighthouse is incredibly important because it's make or break at the first entrance.'

On first arriving he told Jane that he wanted to work for Lighthouse, that he was good with figures and admin-istration but that he had very little experience of working with people. This was how he described his initital meeting: 'I said that Lighthouse could treat me like a machine because all my life I'd been working like a machine. Then Jane showed me round which I found quite inspirational. I thought she was terribly open and gentle, so I decided to tell her that I was positive. She didn't bat an eyelid, of course, which I was very pleased about, but then I found myself beginning to feel rather overwhelmed by everything. So she sat me down and I felt these tears coming to my eyes. I tried to pull myself together because after all I'd come to offer my services not to ask for sympathy.

'But I felt immediately at ease and at home at Lighthouse. It was the first place I'd felt free enough to be myself and Jane was the first person I felt able to reveal my status to. After that, Lighthouse became my motivation. In fact, if it hadn't been for Lighthouse I think I'd have lain in bed all day and done nothing with my life.'

I was struck by the frank and fond relationships people seemed so easily to strike up both among staff and service users. I remember one episode, typical of the place, which occurred when I'd been at Lighthouse only a few days. I was sitting at reception with Jane, when Rosie, a volunteer on the residential unit, burst through the side door in a terrible state. A very close friend of hers had just died of AIDS, she'd had to arrange the funeral single-handedly, she had been involved in a car accident over the weekend and had just come back from seeing her boyfriend who had offered her neither support nor sympathy. Jane understood immediately that something was wrong and took her in her arms while Rosie sobbed uncontrollably. It was significant, I thought, that Rosie had not been on duty that day and yet had come to Lighthouse because she knew this was the one place where people would listen to her and ease her distress.

I soon realised that the reason why I felt so immediately enmeshed in the place was because formality was dispensed with when you were living and working with people with AIDS. There simply wasn't the time to undo the packaging slowly and cautiously. Emotions were raw and vulnerable because loss was an everyday occurrence, and there was a great deal of hugging and kissing because too often people with AIDS were seen as unlovable and untouchable.

It occurred to me that if I stayed at Lighthouse long enough it might be very good for me. Although I feel love and affection easily and have no difficulty expressing it in words, I have never been very good at demonstrating it in a physical sense except with those closest to me. I have always envied people who are tactile, who seem to feel perfectly at ease holding and hugging others.

Sheila, who was a volunteer at Lighthouse during the PortaKabin days and worked as the admissions assistant on the unit, was amazed when she got involved with the organisation: 'I thought they were round the bend,' she told me. 'I'd come from a very disciplined, straight establishment background; I was married and had been running my own business for thirty years and it all seemed very casual and embarrassing seeing people kiss each other on the lips. I remember the first day I started working there one of the organisers asked me if I wanted a cuddle and I said yes because I didn't know what else to say but I thought it was the most extraordinary thing that people went around cuddling each other.' Sheila was not the sort of woman you rushed up to and threw your arms around – being fairly formidable in her direct, no-nonsense approach – but she had changed a lot from those early days. Once I saw her running towards a volunteer she was particularly fond of, calling 'Jimmy, you're back and I've missed you so much' and then enveloping him in a long and heartfelt embrace.

I soon learnt that some people didn't like being kissed. One volunteer said, 'I wish he would stop doing that,' when a very attractive young man came up and gave him a long drawn-out kiss. And one of the closest friends I made at Lighthouse admitted to me that in his first year of working there he had kissed, and allowed himself to be kissed, by just about everybody, but now he'd come to the conclusion that it was better to be more selective because he felt assuming intimacy through a hug or a kiss was misleading and intrusive behaviour.

In the early days of HIV infection, it was felt that people with the virus should be hugged and touched because most people in society wouldn't go near them, but soon the absurdity of this notion became apparent since many people didn't like being hugged and kissed by everyone they met. Jeff, a volunteer on the residential unit, told me of a distressing experience that had happened to him: 'I'd been talking for a long while with one of the residents who was very upset about something. He'd been telling me that he was a very tactile person so when I got up to leave I asked him if I could kiss him. I don't know whether it was out of compassion, love, pity or lust but he agreed and I kissed him on the lips. When I was leaving that evening I came to say goodbye and kissed him again on the lips, but this time I was pulled up sharply by him when he told me in a controlled but fairly hostile voice, "Please, Jeff, never do that again. I only like my friends to kiss me."'

I felt for Jeff when he told me this story: he was obviously mortified by the experience. There were few volunteers as caring and well-meaning as he, and this unexpected slap in the face was a severe blow to his confidence. Sometimes I too didn't know how far to go with a resident. Once I was walking down the corridor when I saw a female volunteer lying on the bed with a young man who had recently succumbed to meningitis and as a result didn't know who or where he was. This woman was gently rocking the man in her arms and stroking his brow. It was a touching scene but left me feeling just a little bit uneasy – because I knew I would have been too self-conscious to show such demonstrative and spontaneous affection myself. I felt slightly envious of this woman whom I subsequently came to know and like a lot. She was big, open-hearted and all-embracing in her manner and her way of dealing with this very confused person was the way she would have dealt with any child or elderly person.

Whether it was appropriate behaviour, however, I am not so sure. Some months later we were together at a meeting for volunteers when the person responsible for centre volunteers spoke about boundaries and mentioned the fact that some volunteers were too tactile with residents. There had apparently been one or two complaints and the whole question of boundaries obviously needed to be looked at. It so happened that on that very day I had been sitting with someone who was terminally ill. He was unconscious of what was going on around him, although he may well have been aware of my presence. As I sat there I wondered what, if anything, I should do. He had beautiful, long, thin, motionless hands and I considered taking one of them in mine as a sign of support and affection. However, I didn't, partly because it would have made me feel uncomfortable, but also because I was aware that this man had no redress. In other words, there was no way in which he could tell me not to take hold of his hand if he didn't like it and, therefore, the action was potentially intrusive.

There were no rules where this was concerned. You had to use your own judgment and sensitivity. I tended to err on the cautious side and stand back in moments of uncertainty, even though I knew my behaviour might have been misconstrued as aloof or unfriendly.

But in a society like ours where people don't easily touch or show affection, I found London Lighthouse an extremely healthy environment to be in because people were mostly willing and able to show emotion. As a volunteer, I felt the most important thing was to be perceptive to people's wants and needs. Touch was still vitally important. One woman with AIDS told me that she had broken down in tears in a supermarket queue when she'd felt the breath of a stranger on her neck because it was the first hint of human contact she'd had for over a year.

In his pamphlet 'AIDS: An Issue for Everyone' published in 1986 Christopher Spence writes: 'Closeness, emotional and physical, is a rational human need. We have also learned that it provides an essential contradiction to early isolation and separation. The opportunity to enjoy relaxed physical intimacy with another person who cherishes us will often bring to the surface for release painful emotion associated with early deprivation of the closeness we needed as very young people. But closeness and sex tend to be confused in our society, and because of this confusion deep intimacy, except in a sexual context – and not always then – is generally in short supply. In the face of AIDS and the current widespread fear of it, so much of which is only revived old fear (of disease, disfigurement, pain, death etc.), people are more than usually terrified to get close and the tendency to retreat into, and act out, old isolation can run riot.'

In a talk Christopher Spence gave early in 1990, he outlined another important aspect of London Lighthouse philosophy – namely the reciprocal nature of relationships between those providing and those receiving care. In it he said: 'It is easy sometimes in the day-to-day pressure of delivering services, whatever they may be, to forget that the relationships between those who deliver care and those who receive it are real relationships in which, like all real relationships, there must be true reciprocity. Without reciprocity, and robust mutuality, I don't believe any relationship can be real and therefore mutually empowering. In a real relationship both parties give and receive; love each other, get mad and sometimes have fights, struggle, negotiate with one another, and work towards honesty. These are the relationships which enable people to grow; and if we agree to love people this much, when we lose them because they die or move on, then we have to feel the loss, let our hearts break, grieve and mend, growing ourselves in the process. Without this reciprocity I believe our care, sooner or later, withers and becomes ineffective.'

One member of the management team thought that some things about Lighthouse were maddeningly ethereal such as the notion of unconditional love and support. 'Love is such an easily misconstrued word,' she said. 'You can be respectful, have compassion, have empathy, but how can you possibly love everyone?' And I heard Christopher Spence criticised for being too simplistic and idealistic in his vision of creating a loving, respectful and unoppressive place of safety which focused on empowering people to live as well and fully as possible.

Spence, however, had never for a moment suggested that the notion of a loving, respectful and unoppressive place of safety was one that could be easily achieved. He had indeed repeatedly challenged people's confusion between loving and liking, encouraging people to understand that loving people was nothing to do with being 'nice' to them, nor even necessarily with accommodating their wishes, but something much more subtle and complex to do with a willingness to pay attention, to offer equality and respect, and a willingness to think with, rather than for, people.

The primary focus of London Lighthouse's work was the empowerment of people affected by HIV and AIDS, and the project's activities were expressed through three main commitments, known as the vision statement. Firstly, to build into all its operations time and space for the giving and receiving of care and attention between individuals and groups. Secondly, to work to change engrained social attitudes which collude to deny that death and dying are central facets of life and living. Thirdly, to address and challenge all related issues of prejudice and oppression.

In the first ever *Leading Lights* newsletter, which came out in December 1986, Christopher Spence wrote: 'London Lighthouse is here to assist us to lead the lives we want, and to let the light of hopeful possibility shine in the face of so much gloom.' It was a radical statement and like the vision statement went further than any other AIDS organisation worldwide had done before.

Some people saw the vision statement as a source of inspiration so that although much had to change before the vision could be realised it was a yardstick by which they could measure what was happening at Lighthouse. 'In a way it's like a soppy religious model,' one member of staff told me. 'Yet it never fails to inspire me and if something happens in the organisation that I'm not happy with I'll always bring it back to these guiding principles to see if it fits.'

But many people struggled to keep the vision statement at the heart of London Lighthouse. With such laudable ideals it was hardly surprising that at times it got buried under the kind of brawling and back-biting present in any young, expanding organisation, and especially in one dealing with such an emotive issue as AIDS. Some people thought that Lighthouse hadn't even begun to change attitudes or eliminate injustice and maybe it couldn't hope to do so when a single picture of Princess Diana shaking the hand of a person with AIDS had probably done more to change engrained social attitudes than the many years of hard work put in by every one of the AIDS organisations.

London Lighthouse expressed its commitment to empowerment by having people with HIV and AIDS working at every level of the organisation as well as by an explicit undertaking to consult with people using the services on all major matters of policy. To Christopher Spence empowerment meant: 'Seeing and treating the individual receiving care as central, and as far as possible autonomous, fully in charge of the decision-making process; it means working with rather than for people using the services; and it means allowing time and attention, as much as is required, in the process of delivering care for the individual's own intuitive and emotional process to be enabled.'

At one of Lighthouse's weekly open days, a Swedish doctor, astonished at the ease with which the issues of death and dying were addressed, asked about Lighthouse's human resource management, and about how the organisation succeeded in keeping staff motivated. I was amazed that every member of the panel, which always included people living with HIV and AIDS, as well as nurses and other workers, said essentially the same thing: that at Lighthouse they were challenged to develop new skills and to give of their best; they learnt to offer and receive support and, like it or not, to deal with painful emotion, especially in the face of loss. They all said that this was not easy, that there were no recipes, but that they thought it was this above all which kept everyone empowered and which drew people like a magnet to the project, probably accounting also for a very low staff turnover.

· *Four* ·

While most of what took place in the reception area was of a fairly routine and straightforward nature, with people behaving in a reasonable and inconspicuous manner, as a volunteer new to the organisation, I could not fail to notice those making most noise or in the greatest distress first.

I witnessed many volatile scenes in the reception area and very often the centre support workers had to intervene to prevent such situations from becoming explosive. Disruptive behaviour was often just a cry for attention but the trouble was that it did not help to create a safe environment and in extreme cases people actually had to be suspended from the building because they were seen to be jeopardising other people's safety. The dilemma for all workers was, do I help someone who is in such dire need of help even at the risk of alienating others, or do I keep this a safe – and some would say cosy – environment?

Everyone had their own ideas about who needed the most help, especially in the drop-in area. For instance, there was one man with the virus who had been banned from the building for biting and shouting, and a member of staff told me that she hadn't been frightened of him and didn't agree with the ban. 'I wish more had gone into the decision and that someone had consulted the centre support workers first,' she said. 'Management just decided on the ban but didn't think about the effect it would have on the people who had to carry it out.' This particular ex-service user still occasionally managed to get through the doors by slipping in behind someone else and his deportation always caused a great deal of unpleasantness. He had a severe drinking problem which would culminate in acts of violence and as a result the police were frequently called.

Violence, I discovered, was not an uncommon occurrence at Lighthouse. I was working on the desk once when we were warned by the residential unit that a man with a shot gun might try and gain entrance to the building. Apparently he had had a brief affair with a resident who was refusing to see him again and he had therefore threatened to come in and blow his ex-lover's brains out. Another time I discovered that a young man called Brendon, who was a service user, had come to visit his boyfriend on the unit but when he was told that his boyfriend wouldn't see him, he went berserk and tried to slit his wrists. Luckily the damage was only superficial and, once a nurse had seen to him, he was sent home. Later, however, he came back. On being told that his boyfriend still didn't want to see him, he lay down in the middle of the road waiting for a car to hit him. The last I heard of him was that he had been taken to hospital with minor injuries.

Another tricky customer was Stan whom I first came across on my third day at Lighthouse when I noticed a dirty and unshaven man in his early forties hanging around the building. He was obviously new to the building and no one knew why he was there until he came up to the desk and asked when the NA (Narcotics Anonymous) meeting was due to begin. He then shook everyone by the hand and introduced himself as Stan. Later that day he came and sat by the desk looking cross and lost: he couldn't decide whether to stay for the meeting (which didn't start for another three hours) or to leave. In the end he left half an hour before the meeting was due to begin.

But he was in again the following day, drugged or drunk I wasn't sure which. This time he was very loud and aggressive and started reciting poetry – his own compositions – some of which were surprisingly good. There was something terribly sad about him. He could have been a very good-looking man had he not abused his body so and he was clearly no fool. When it came to Stan, the patience of people working on reception amazed me. 'If we're not busy and he's not upsetting anyone then we'll listen,' said John, one of the part-time staff on reception. When Stan told me he hadn't eaten for days I tried to organise a free meal voucher for him but discovered in the process that free meals were only available to people known to have HIV. Stan, as far as we knew, had not been tested.

Once he knew he had found a moderately sympathetic audience Stan came in most days after that even though he wasn't exactly greeted with open arms. At first most service users seemed to tolerate him, managing to ignore his extremely bizarre behaviour. Once he stood in front of the desk and stared at us with a glazed and fixed expression for at least ten minutes.

Sometimes he sat for ages on the chair by reception. In the end we had to tell him to go and sit elsewhere because he was intimidating people by eavesdropping on their conversations. He could be charming but equally he could be extremely annoying and sometimes even aggressive, so not surprisingly service users eventually began to complain about his unpredictable nature.

The problem with Stan became steadily worse until the management became aware that his occasionally ferocious behaviour was beginning to offend those who came to Lighthouse seeking some peace and quiet. The question of what to do with him was raised at a meeting where it was decided that initially the most important thing was for everyone to adopt consistent behaviour when dealing with him, in other words to remind him that this was a centre for people with HIV and AIDS, not to allow him to sit in the chair next to the reception desk and not to be too accommodating or too friendly. John handled him well. When I heard Stan ask him to go fishing with him at the weekend, John was very polite and, without being in the least bit patronising, just told him he couldn't go because he had to work at the weekend.

Inevitably Stan was eventually banned from the building for insulting and seriously upsetting another service user. He took it surprisingly well and left hailing everyone in a jocular fashion with the words, 'May God live in your hearts'.

But, as many had suspected, he returned the next day and tried to gain access once again. For precisely this reason London Lighthouse's main entrance consisted of an outer and inner door. The outer door was open twenty-four hours a day, and the inner door was locked and opened by remote control at the discretion of the person working behind the desk. It was only on rare occasions such as this that the door was not opened. So Stan was trapped between the two doors hurling abuse at staff and at anyone who found their way blocked by him. He said he thought the ban had only lasted for a day and then shouted through the partition: 'Does this mean that my offspring are banned and my offspring's offspring?' When he realised he was not going to be allowed back in he left screaming defiantly, 'May you all rot in hell.' And as a final flaunting gesture he stuck his head back through the door and yelled, 'I hate all you poofs anyway.'

When the two-door blocking system was first devised for reasons of security, there was a lot of criticism from people who felt it was inhibitory and contrary to Lighthouse's open-door policy. If you bar one person from the building – the argument went – where will it stop? And who was to say what exactly constituted offensive behaviour? However, most people agreed that the way Stan conducted himself was offensive and sometimes threatening. One man with the virus told me he thought it made a mockery of the whole ethos of the place that Stan had been allowed to stay so long when all he had done was upset and intimidate service users. 'Imagine a newly diagnosed person coming into Lighthouse for the first time – frightened, intimidated and in shock,' he said. 'What would your first impression be on walking through the door and seeing this man pacing three steps forward and four steps back, reciting mindless poetry to himself? This is a drop-in centre, not a drop-out centre,' he said.

A lot of debate preceded the decision to suspend Stan from the building because on the one hand London Lighthouse wanted and needed to open its doors to the local community but on the other hand one of its primary aims was to be a non-oppressive place of safety for people affected by HIV and AIDS. In Stan's case it was difficult to ascertain at first whether he was a potential service user because of the many sensitive issues around confidentiality and HIV. Because of this, staff on reception were often in a very difficult and vulnerable position, unable to confront people about why they were there and having to put up with a great deal of anti-social behaviour.

Service users who had not been to the building for a while sometimes complained that it was not as safe a place as it had once been. This was inevitable since it had started out as a predominantly middle-class gay man's initiative. The change had also been noted in the residential wing. A nurse who had been working on the unit for two years said that at the beginning the clientele were quite different: 'It largely consisted of gay men (since this was the population group most affected in London) who had a lot of knowlege about AIDS, understood their medication and knew what was happening to them. But that's changed now, probably because more people are finding themselves positive.'

Although Lighthouse appeared now to be attracting a cross-section of the HIV population, there were still many people who had not heard of it, and, even among those who had heard of it, many did not dare enter its doors. This attitude was not only due to prejudice or misconceived notions but also because some people did not want to be a part of such a high-profile place which was publicly addressing and challenging issues around HIV and AIDS. This applied particularly to women and drug users, as well as to whole families affected by the virus whose lives had been decimated by the physical and emotional effects of HIV, as well as by the stigma attached to it. Everyone who walked through the door of Lighthouse was making a statement and some people believed such a statement to be an entirely destructive and counterproductive act. For these people self-protection was paramount and could be achieved only by concealing the very thing which was tearing their lives apart.

Despite this there were also many more drug users

using the services than ever before. When I was working on reception, a young and bedraggled-looking couple came in with their three-year-old son, both seemed completely comatose. They came to the desk demanding something but I couldn't make out what it was they were asking for. They had to repeat the question three times before I realised that what they wanted was a plastic bag in which to put disposable needles. A more experienced volunteer who was listening to this exchange understood exactly what was going on and unhesitatingly supplied them with a bag, though he instructed them to return it to the desk immediately after use. With an increasing number of drug users being diagnosed HIV positive, Lighthouse's client group had inevitably changed and staff and volunteers were having to alert themselves to how best to cater for their needs.

By 1991 as many as 15 per cent of service users were drug users. Some gay men who had been coming in for respite care since the unit opened had noticed the change with disquiet. One man told me: 'There's an uneasy mix between the two client groups and as a result Lighthouse isn't the warm and friendly place it once was.' Certainly there was a wide and visible gap between the gay and drug-using communities and you could usually tell who belonged to which. When I attended the 1991 Annual Conference we split up into several workshops and at the end of the day the facilitator's assistant from each workshop had to report back to the assembly the key points and recommendations made by each group. When it was the turn of the gay men's group, a man stood up and in a brazenly honest display of anger read out a statement saying that London Lighthouse no longer catered for gay men and in so doing had become a part of gay oppression.

This dissatisfaction was not a new occurrence, I discovered. There had always been criticism of Lighthouse's expressed intention to make its services accessible to every population group affected by HIV and AIDS. Spence had repeatedly challenged gay men to accept that this commitment to diversity was not only right but ultimately also in their best interests and that the resource implications within Lighthouse were something that they had to work out together. However, he also conceded that perhaps in the recent past Lighthouse had not paid enough attention to gay men's needs.

While I was at Lighthouse, staff were being retrained and were learning to adapt to the needs of drug users – for some this meant a radical change of emphasis in the way they worked. For nurses on the unit it meant coping with chaotic behaviour as well as chronic disease, and the inevitable consequence of this was that for some the unit was no longer a safe working environment. Also, service users who had used the drop-in area since Lighthouse's opening, felt the atmosphere had changed, becoming less safe and less welcoming. These were all fairly negative assertions, and undoubtedly Lighthouse could have been a cosier, easier place to inhabit had it continued to cater almost exclusively for gay men, but ultimately it would have been untenable to exclude heterosexual men, women and chidren when one of Lighthouse's primary commitments was 'to build into its operation time and space for the giving and receiving of care and attention between individuals and groups'.

One day when I was doing a morning shift on reception I got talking to Alice who was a twenty-four-year-old drug user staying on the residential unit for two weeks. She told me that she'd always known about AIDS but, when she first started using at the age of eighteen, sharing needles was what everyone did and it didn't strike her as important to curtail her behaviour until three years later. Even then she noticed that the talk was always almost exclusively about how the virus could be passed on intravenously rather than sexually. She told me how it had all begun: 'My father started abusing me at the age of five and continued to do so all through my childhood and into my teens. I knew he liked big women because he was always eyeing up the ones who had big tits and rolls of fat, so at the age of twelve I decided that if I became thin then he wouldn't find me attractive anymore.' So Alice stopped eating, lost two and a half stone in weight and prayed for her father to stop abusing her. But he didn't, and fifteen years later she still looked desperately under-nourished having subsequently suffered from severe anorexia nervosa.

At the age of sixteen she started taking heroin because a friend said it would calm her exam nerves. It did but once the exams were over she couldn't leave it alone and from there began a life of squatting, petty crime and disastrous relationships. She had been in prison several times and, contrary to every other ex-prisoner I met, said she had been treated well by staff precisely because she was HIV positive.

'I was given a cell of my own. I was allowed to keep the door open during the day, I could use the recreational facilities at any time and I didn't have to work. But it was very important that other inmates shouldn't know that I was positive because they would have given me a very hard time. It's only in Scotland that prisoners are more accepting of HIV, probably because there's so much around.'

After prison Alice moved to Scunthorpe where she lived on an estate with her boyfriend who was also HIV positive and also an addict. Their neighbours somehow discovered that they were living next door to a couple of 'AIDS victims' and so formed themselves into a group of vigilantes and began systematically to terrorise.

'First came hate mail – written in thick red paint supposed to resemble blood. They said if we didn't move out someone would see to it that we would "disappear". Then, one day, I came home and found our cat lying dead outside the main entrance. She was so smashed up I reckon they'd thrown her from the top floor of the block. A few days later someone put burning oil under our door. In the end we had to move because we were so frightened. These people weren't the type to stop at threats and we knew the police wouldn't help us. We'd never caused our neighbours any trouble since we rarely had friends over and we never played loud music, but they hated us all the same because in their eyes we had AIDS and were contagious – unfit to inhabit the same planet as them. They were obviously terrified of us, you could see it in their eyes. People would climb up thirty flights of stairs in order to avoid sharing a lift with us.'

Alice's voice was slow and slurred. She seemed barely to know where she was or where she was going next and yet she told her story with remarkable precision. After years of addiction and with the first signs of HIV illness now showing, her life seemed bereft and bankrupt. Lighthouse had offered her a warm room, wholesome food and much needed friendship but it was her only oasis in a large and barren wilderness. Although no one knew for certain what would happen to Alice, the general feeling was that once she'd left Lighthouse she would sink rapidly further into the abyss.

For a while after she left the unit she would return to the drop-in centre, sometimes remarkably buoyant and at other times listless and despondent. When she was like this she would sit in the smoking area chain-smoking, staring at the wall ahead of her without uttering a word. When she was cheerful she would talk about her plans for the future – holidays she wanted to take and new money-earning projects she intended to get involved in. She came to Lighthouse because she knew it was a place where she could find peace and where no one would hassle her.

Her drug addiction seemed much more central to her life than her HIV status. She said to me once that if it hadn't been for being tested positive, she would probably be dead by now because her diagnosis had made her seek help from various drug dependency units and HIV centres. In other words she felt that HIV had prolonged her life. But there was very little quality to her life and her mind seemed as tortured as her disintegrating body. Everything she did took enormous effort and left her breathless and exhausted. It was no surprise to me that one day without warning Alice stopped coming to Lighthouse. I knew it was a bad sign but I never managed to find out what exactly had happened to her.

I never felt that my dealings with Alice were very fruitful. Sometimes when she described the persecution she was experiencing in her street or when she sat in a heap unable to move from pain in her joints, I found I had nothing to say to her. So we would just sit in silence while I hoped that some words of comfort would eventually emerge from my cluttered brain. People like Alice, who were barely coping and living so close to the edge, made me at times feel despairing and superfluous.

In time and with training I became better equipped at handling people who were very acutely distressed. I learnt that the most important thing was to listen, but to listen in such a way that you heard what a person was saying as well as what a person was not saying. A lot of people in distress say only half of what they really want to say hoping that the person listening to them will somehow pick up the message. Reasoning and logic are inappropriate at the initial stage of shock and could indeed have a markedly negative effect. If someone is convinced their world is coming to an end, they want you to agree with them and not deny it. This means valuing and respecting that person by being with them 100 per cent and not becoming distracted or letting your mind wander on to other things.

People exhibited certain kinds of behaviour depending on how they were feeling. It was very important for those working on the ground floor to know how someone presented when they were angry, depressed or demented. For example, the less I confronted aggressive behaviour the less I would confront that person's anger and the more I'd be able to deal with what was going on underneath. Anger would present itself as straightforward verbal abuse, or in abrasive and threatening behaviour, or even passively in which case it was much more difficult to identify. It was also all about reading signs and understanding things about myself because the way I reacted came in part from my own experience of these emotional states and in part from the way I perceived things to be.

· *Five* ·

Apart from providing day care, community services, residential services, a counselling service, a drop-in centre and cafe, London Lighthouse played host to numerous groups and events which had a connection with AIDS or gay issues. On my first Sunday working as a volunteer there was a Body Positive celebration, a women's meeting which no one turned up to and a discussion on homophobia in the media. Weekends were usually quiet and this Sunday was no exception. One of the few people to come up to the reception desk was a short, stocky, middle-aged woman who came in off the street. She was nervous, distracted and unable to look me in the eye. Those with more experience than myself knew instantly that she was potential trouble, but despite this she was treated with the utmost courtesy. She was clutching an old carrier bag inside of which she proudly showed me were two quails, a few mouldy Brussels sprouts and two rashers of streaky bacon wrapped in foil. She had brought them, she said, for Patrick O'Connor who was staying on the residential unit.

One of the first rules when dealing with a request like this from a member of the public was to ascertain first whether that person was using Lighthouse services and, if they were, whether they wished to see the visitor concerned. This was done for reasons of confidentiality and it was an important if laborious process.

In the case of Patrick O'Connor I didn't have to go through this rigmarole as there was no one on the unit by that name, or anything remotely like it, nor had there ever been. The woman wasn't satisfied with this answer and told me he often went under other names and offered a description. She said he was six feet two inches tall, may or may not have had an Irish accent because he changed it according to his mood, and he was 'devastatingly good looking'. I rang the unit again but was told there was no one staying who fitted that description. Reluctantly she handed over the quails and Brussels sprouts for me to give to the kitchens, keeping only a half-drunk bottle of whisky for herself, and promptly left.

Half an hour later she was back, but this time in an angry mood and demanding we return the coat she'd delivered to Patrick O'Connor the previous week. We looked for the coat but couldn't find it and I'm afraid I assumed she was both a time waster and a story teller. But I was wrong – the coat did eventually materialise – she had indeed brought it for the mysterious Patrick O'Connor whom no one had ever seen or heard of. Begrudgingly she grabbed hold of it and left for the second time.

Ten minutes later she was back again, this time in more somber mood. She pointed at the blue donkey jacket she was wearing and told me that he had given it to her: 'Just imagine,' she said, 'he's giving his clothes away as if he were going to die, but he isn't. He even gave me his rosary. I must find him because I really did love him you know.' There was nothing I could say, no words of reassurance I could give her. Even if Patrick O'Connor had been a resident I somehow doubt if he would have wanted to see her, so eventually there was nothing left for her to do but disappear into the streets of Notting Hill – this time not to reappear.

The atmosphere in the drop-in centre was changeable – it could be both playful and intense. Playful because this was where friends gathered to gossip and pass the time of day, and intense because a great deal of loss and sadness was also experienced here. Sometimes this intensity was quite stifling. For instance, one day I was working at reception when I became aware of a solitary figure sitting on a single seat near the front entrance. He was sobbing silently and made no attempt to brush aside the tears which rolled down his cheeks. Someone passed him a box of tissues and stroked his back but made a point of not intruding on his sadness. Then one of the nuns who volunteered at Lighthouse and who knew him well noticed his distress and drew a chair up close to him. Without saying a word, she took him in her arms. It was a private scene happening in a public place and though most people had observed the man, no one seemed shocked or embarrassed by this sudden display of emotion.

For the first few weeks of my time at London Lighthouse I sat behind the reception desk and watched events unfold before my eyes. I got introduced to everyone and soon could put names to faces and faces to names. But I felt as if I was on the fringes, only able to see a partial picture. It was rather like catching snippets of a drama, or snippets of many dramas, and not being able to discover how it began or where it ended. The grounded and secure feeling I had came from the people I was working with, volunteers and staff alike, some of whom had the virus and some of whom did not.

A lot of people who worked and used the services at Lighthouse felt this way. I saw people arrive in a dejected and depressed state and within days of coming to the centre I saw them revived. It wasn't that they'd had massive doses of counselling or complementary therapies, it was simply that they'd come and met people who were willing to listen and share experiences. Some had assumed Lighthouse would be a depressing place where people only talked about what drug they were taking or what infection they were fighting and were therefore pleasantly surprised to find the atmosphere more like that of a club or cafe than an institution.

Andrew was a good example of someone whose whole life seemed to change when he came to Lighthouse. I was working on the desk the first day he came in. He was round-faced and wide-eyed and wearing jeans and a white T-shirt. He told me later that he was thirty-nine but he looked much younger. He had been diagnosed as having AIDS six months previously when suddenly and unexpectedly he was rushed to hospital with Pneumocystis Carinii Pneumonia (PCP). He recovered quickly but when he got home he discovered his lover had left him and he'd been given the sack from his job as manager of a men's clothes shop. For several months Andrew went underground – shocked, demoralised and scared of what would happen next. Eventually he found his way to Lancaster Road because he remembered a friend having spoken of it as 'the most exclusive place to die in town'.

On the first day that Andrew came to Lighthouse, I watched him tentatively move round the ground floor area. He didn't speak to anyone, or read any of the literature on display, nor did he drink or eat anything. He seemed to be soaking it all in. His face was expressionless and I couldn't make out whether he felt comfortable or so awkward that he didn't know how to get up and go. Occasionally someone would ask him if he was all right at which he would nod politely but resist from entering into further conversation.

The next day Andrew was back again. It was a creative knitting day and the woman who taught it persuaded him to take hold of a pair of needles. It turned out he'd been knitting since the age of five and once had even designed sweaters for a living. Although he still said very little, he looked more at ease and on his way out he bought several Lighthouse badges which he attached proudly to his jacket.

He came in every day after that, staying several hours but always leaving before the evening rush hour. After about the fourth day everyone knew who he was, and after the first week he could be found languishing on one of the sofas in the smoking area with people gathered all around him listening to his stories. His oblique sense of humour and his ability to mimic and tell stories made him a popular entertainer. Like a number of the gay men I met with AIDS, he was able to drag a surprising amount of humour out of the topic. 'I've always wanted to be in on everything to do with the gay lifestyle,' he said, 'so I guess I'd have been a bit peeved if I hadn't been diagnosed positive.' He was brave too. He didn't mind who knew of his status. Once, on his way to Lighthouse, a bus conductor looked at his disabled pass and said in an accusing tone, 'You don't look disabled.' Without flinching and without showing any sign of embarrassment or anger, Andrew looked him in the eyes and said for all to hear, 'Well, you're wrong actually, I've got AIDS.'

It wasn't long before Andrew, like many before him, became a part of the fixtures and fittings of Lighthouse. He knew everybody's name, what they did, how long they'd been working there or using the services, as well as any gossip attached to them. He was one of the first to find out why a member of staff had been sacked for gross misconduct. I observed with interest how his clothes changed over the months. Having initially dressed rather soberly, later he came in every day wearing something which was more colourful and showy. Most people got on well with him, though there was also a feeling that he was rather too much of a chameleon. One member of staff told me she felt wary of anyone who took over the place quite so quickly.

It wasn't that Lighthouse changed Andrew, it was just that it brought him back to how he had always been, which was loud, boisterous, generous and gay (in the original sense of the word). Because of this there were times when his presence exasperated me and when I wished he possessed just a degree more sensitivity and discretion. Overall, though, I found him a potent example of someone struggling, and succeeding, to live well with AIDS.

In training I had been told that working on the desk was sometimes difficult and demanding. Reception staff had recently been renamed 'centre support workers' in order to reflect the more involved nature of their work. Working at reception at London Lighthouse was very different from working at reception in most other organisations where it was often only a matter of giving out information, receiving incoming mail and pointing people in the right direction. At Lighthouse, centre support workers were often the first port of call for people in extreme distress, some of whom had only recently been diagnosed and consequently had nowhere to go.

London Lighthouse's approach to management was

people-based, consultative and participative, while at the same time having an entirely conventional structure. So while setting up an apparently traditional hierarchical structure, emphasising clarity of role, authority in decision making, defined areas of responsibility and managerial accountability, it was committed to managing the organisation in a way which fostered a co-operative approach to work and encouraged the participation of everyone in the decision-making process. There were also numerous mechanisms for people to say what they thought on every issue, as well as access to good supervision, training, professional development and personal support. These ranged from formal structures like the Annual Conference, the Consultative Forum (made up of elected representatives from every level in the structure) and the Equal Opportunities Action Team, to many informal working groups, involving people with different roles and from different levels, in thinking and recommending change.

It struck me that at Lighthouse this traditional management pyramid structure was often turned on its head with the people who were working on a one-to-one level with service users being given, in effect, the greatest responsibility. Reception staff, for instance, were situated on the front line, because what they said or did when someone walked through the door determined whether or not that person stayed or left, and since the support of service users was vital to the existence of the whole organisation, then these workers had a great deal of responsibility and influence.

One very quickly became adept at spotting those who needed help but didn't know how to ask for it. When I'd only been at Lighthouse for three days a young man came into the building, walked round the reception area briskly two or three times and finally stopped and stood reading the notices for several minutes. He was on his way out when I caught his eye and asked him if he wanted any help. 'I think I've got the wrong address,' he said. I asked him what address he wanted but he wouldn't tell me. So I told him where he was and explained that London Lighthouse was a centre for people facing the challenge of AIDS – which is how it is described on the foundation stone. Somehow this broke the ice. Saying one had come to the wrong address, I discovered, was one of the most common opening lines.

I found myself initially treating service users with kid gloves and assuming that they were all brave, admirable and likeable individuals. It was an attitude which, in its endeavour to see all things good in people with AIDS, couldn't help but be patronising. The truth was, of course – and I realised this all too quickly – that service users, like anyone else, varied enormously in their appeal.

One young man of not more than twenty strode into the building one day wearing a bright canary-coloured suit. He made a beeline for one of the volunteers working on reception, who obviously knew him well. She asked him if he was happy, to which he nodded and grinned, showing her an air ticket which he had just bought for Amsterdam. 'I'm going there at the weekend for a drugs extravaganza,' he told her blithely. Once he'd walked off, I asked the volunteer who he was. 'Oh dear,' she said, 'that's Morton. He's a service user and a terrible, terrible pain.'

Five minutes later he was back, upset now because his former partner who was staying on the unit would not see him. 'Have you any idea why I can't go up?' he asked plaintively. The volunteer was patient and reassuring: you would never have suspected she found him so difficult. 'It just happens like that sometimes,' she said. 'Why don't you come back and try again tomorrow.' This calmed him down for about twenty minutes during which he moved restlessly round the ground floor unable to settle to anything for more than a few moments.

When he returned to the desk he requested to see a nurse immediately. If I'd been alone on the desk I probably would have rung up to the unit, but the volunteer knew that this was just another attention-seeking ploy, and she suggested that he went to see his own GP instead. He finally left saying he was going off to St Mary's Hospital, Paddington.

There was no attempt by anybody at any time to pretend that Morton wasn't anything but demanding and irritating but at the same time staff seemed genuinely fond of him. Their attempts to help him came not from a hypocritical benevolent attitude but rather from genuine concern for someone who was really still only a boy – desperately in need of attention and affection and basking in the fact that Lighthouse was giving it to him.

It was not unknown for someone to walk up and down Lancaster Road several times before coming into the building. Once inside and having spoken to one of the reception staff, they might then eat or drink something in the cafe where any misconceptions they might have about the place would immediately be invalidated because here they saw people with AIDS eating and drinking alongside people who did not have AIDS, using the same plates and the same cutlery. From reception someone was usually directed to the information service where he or she would be told about services available at London Lighthouse and elsewhere. A typical service user's route through the building would then continue to the counselling department, and on to the support groups, day care and relaxation classes, finally culminating in the residential unit.

Not everyone who used the drop-in area was HIV

positive. There were a few people who came in everyday and used Lighthouse like a social club. At first I wondered whether this should be encouraged since the pleasant surroundings, comfortable furniture and free teas three times a week were surely meant for more needy individuals, but as the weeks went by, I realised that actually only a very few people like this used the building and that they were indeed a great asset to the place since Lighthouse did not believe in segregating the sick from the well, nor did it believe in segregating those affected by AIDS from those who were not affected. The bottom line was that everyone was affected, and those who thought it had nothing to do with them were likely to be the most at risk. The more that local residents used the cafe and drop-in centre, the closer Lighthouse would come to achieving its goal of changing engrained social attitudes.

Suzi, the centre support co-ordinator, believed, for instance, that groups of young boys should be allowed in Lighthouse as long as they maintained reasonable behaviour. One evening at about 7 p.m. a group of fourteen-year-old black youths tried to gain entrance but were trapped between the two doors. One of them asked Suzi, 'Does everyone have AIDS here?' and before she had time to reply another one chimed in, 'Will I catch AIDS if I come in?' Their sneering manner made Suzi hesitate before she allowed them to enter but she did so because, as she said later, 'I don't want to collude with other people's issues around black youths. If people don't feel safe with young black men then they have to look at the issue and think why. There are lots of people who don't think they should be allowed in but if you exclude people like that it only feeds the ignorance and fear and succeeds in reinforcing hostility and mistrust in the community.' On this occasion the boys weren't insulting and in the end they joined a drama group which had only just started; they remained there for twenty minutes only drawing attention to themselves by doing breakdancing instead of the prescribed relaxation exercises.

On another occasion a member of staff refused to let a group of young boys in who had behaved in a rowdy fashion on the previous evening and could only ever be persuaded to leave once they had stuffed their pockets full of free condoms, which lay in plentiful supply on the front desk. This time the boys had a stink bomb device which they hurled through the door, shouting, 'This is for you because you've all got AIDS anyway.'

Later, all through the summer months, I noticed a young mother who would come in every day with her nine-month-old baby. Once I got talking to her I realised she wasn't a service user at all but someone who had lived in the neighbourhood for ten years. Claire liked coming into Lighthouse because she was fed up with the National Childbirth Trust coffee mornings where mothers were obsessively competitive about their children. Having been through the same experience myself, I immediately under-stood what she meant and why Lighthouse provided such a welcome alternative. I too had brought my two-year-old daughter Phoebe there as an alternative way of spend-ing a few enjoyable hours with her.

For several months Claire came in every day, all day. She'd talk to service users, let staff play with her baby, she ate her lunch in the cafe and joined the Friday creative knitting sessions held in the drop-in area. I think she was in need of some friendship during those early months of motherhood, which can be so demanding of one's time and energy, and Lighthouse filled that need. Sadly, people like Claire were all too rare. Not many mothers would want to frequent a place like Lighthouse, let alone allow their baby to be handled and caressed by people with AIDS.

I was having coffee with her sitting out in the garden one humid August morning, with Phoebe playing around the fountain. At one point we saw Jane, one of the most respected and longest-serving volunteers, who was showing round two German medical students. Later she told me they had stopped in their tracks when they saw us. 'You have really achieved so much here,' they said to her. The sight of us two mothers with our two children using the centre just as we might have used one of the cafes in Portobello Road had surprised and moved them.

No day was the same when I was working on reception. Funny, sad, bizarre things happened all the time and I learnt to prepare myself for any eventuality. Of course some of the work was routine and even dull, such as directing people to classes or support groups, looking up telephone numbers, and handing out information leaflets, but there were also days when I would come home unable to leave Lighthouse behind me.

I was amazed that people would actually enter the building not knowing where they were. Perhaps this was a compliment to the architects who had intended to create something quite unlike any other institution. Once I was working on reception when a woman came in selling personal organisers. She obviously thought she had entered just another office development like the one immediately next door. She spoke in a stilted and rehearsed sales patter so that what she was saying made no sense whatsoever.

I couldn't help feeling annoyed at her intrusion and at the inappropriate way in which she was touting her wares, so I told her that we were a charity and not interested in buying her products but if she liked she could leave some information about it on the noticeboard. At this she got out a perfectly hideous pink wind-up toy pig which she let loose on the desk top. 'Why don't you buy one for your girlfriends,' she said, addressing two gay men who happened to be with me at the time. Getting no joy from them, she then turned to me to find out where she was and why she was finding us so uncooperative. So I told her that she was in a centre for people affected by HIV and AIDS. At first she couldn't grasp what I was saying so I had to show it to her written down on an information leaflet. At this her attitude changed instantly. Like so many other anxious and embarrassed people who walked into the building unaware of where they were, she looked horrified and hurriedly packed up her goods and fled.

As she did so she nearly knocked over a tall man in his late thirties, wearing a suit and carrying a brown leather briefcase who was walking boldly towards the desk. He came up to me and said very matter-of-factly, as if he were asking me for the latest information in computer technology, and without lowering his voice one bit, 'I have AIDS. I was diagnosed yesterday and I know nothing about it. Can you help?' I pointed him in the direction of the information office. By contrast, later a man in his mid-forties with very crooked teeth and red eyes came in. He was extremely shaky and spoke so softly that I could hardly hear what he was saying. He had only recently found out that he was HIV positive and on telling his employers had been given the sack, despite twenty-five years loyal service to the firm.

Several hours later a tall and very thin Chinese man arrived to go on the unit. He was with a woman and had brought with him eight bin liners, each one stuffed full of clothes. The woman with him was plainly irritated. 'My mother's in a bad mood today,' he said to me. 'Of course

I'm in a bad mood,' she replied, 'just look at all this junk he's brought with him for only a week's stay.'

The next day a man walked gingerly through the door supported on two sticks. He sat down on the chair by the desk and as I turned to greet him I realised it was someone I had met on my training course. Sadly he was so changed that I barely recognised his face, and I hoped that my shocked expression didn't register as I digested this fact. The encounter made me feel bad on two counts – firstly because I had acted insensitively, albeit instinctively and with no bad intent, and secondly because I had not really taken on board that such things could happen. I knew AIDS had a devastating effect on people's physical appearance but I had no idea that deterioration could take place so rapidly. Three weeks ago I had bumped into this man in the cafe and he had seemed perfectly fit and well.

Very often the whole of the reception area was crowded out by bouquets of flowers so that there was hardly room to move. I was there on the morning of the funeral for a much loved resident called Peter L. One of the volunteers who had become very close to him during his seven-week stay at Lighthouse had come in especially to attend the funeral but when it came to it he couldn't face going because Peter's parents had turned up at the last moment and taken over. Apparently they had caused him such grief during his lifetime, baiting him about his homosexuality and ignoring his illness until he was well into the terminal stages, that this particular volunteer couldn't face the hypocrisy of the event. At one point Mrs L came up to the reception desk thrusting two pink carnations into my hand. 'I'm afraid we can't use these,' she said, raising her eyes to heaven, 'because Peter only wanted yellow and white flowers.' She looked at me in such a way that seemed to suggest her son must have been deranged to have had such bizarre ideas.

You learnt very quickly on reception who were the troublemakers and who the attention seekers. I had a tendency to believe whatever people told me and I had to learn not to be too trusting. Once a woman asked me to lend her a pound. She was a service user who lived locally and who was forever asking to 'borrow' cigarettes, stamps and money. Most people, like myself, gave in because it didn't happen that often and it seemed more sensible to give it to her than to the busker at Notting Hill tube station.

But a member of staff at Lighthouse was very displeased about it. She was adamant that this woman should not have asked for money and accused her of abusing the services at Lighthouse. 'You make it very difficult for people because they feel obliged and that means this isn't a safe place anymore,' she told her. I felt that I had also done wrong in giving this poor woman the money but it was too late now and I hoped she would return it just as she had promised to. No one believed she would, not even me, but to everyone's surprise she did, just two hours later, proving that the strong words of warning had not fallen on deaf ears.

Things happened fast at Lighthouse. I realised this after about five weeks, when already I felt as if I'd been involved in the place for years and people I'd only recently met seemed like old and trusted friends. I kept thinking back to my last experience of working for an organisation. I had been writing for a quarterly specialist magazine – a job I managed to survive for eighteen months despite being intensely unhappy there. It was an office full of unhappy people due to an editor who criticised and thereby undermined the majority of her staff whilst boosting and encouraging the chosen few. I should have left long before I did but, like many others before and after me, my confidence was in tatters and it seemed inconceivable that anyone would ever want to employ me again. Finally, having seen others leave and survive the transition, I too made the break and at long last breathed again.

I was reminded of this ordeal only because it was the last time I had worked for an institution with a traditional management structure, with staff on a pay role who were accountable to their superiors and who were endeavouring to run an organisation in the most efficient and cost-effective way possible. But there the similarities ended. London Lighthouse was the complete antithesis to my former place of employment which was renowned, and still is, for being a particularly hostile environment to work in. There it had been unusual for anyone to say good morning to each other – largely because in an open-plan office people assumed if they said good morning to one person they would have to say it to fifty, and therefore it was simpler not to say it at all. Friendships took months to develop, if they happened at all, and any display of emotion was deemed embarrassing and unprofessional. The words care and support were not part of the vocabulary, and people were basically too closed, too insecure and too lazy to dig deeper than the surface. It wasn't until I came to Lighthouse that I became aware of this and realised exactly why my previous job had been such a dehumanising experience.

Christopher Spence was far more approachable than my previous boss, though not entirely free from criticism. Whenever I was working on reception he would make a point of coming up to the desk to say good morning to us and I often sensed a slight quiver go through the staff, including myself, as we instinctively adopted a somewhat deferential manner, in the way that one does with charismatic leader figures. He was clearly in charge here and my initial impression was that he was both admired and feared – admired for his considerable achievements in getting this project off the ground, and feared because of his somewhat unpredictable nature. While for political and historical reasons he identified as a gay man, he was by now happily married to Nancy Kline with whom he had developed the philosophy (in 'At Least a Hundred Principles of Love') on which London Lighthouse had been based, and who had been closely associated with the project from the start. Although some members of staff had been surprised when he announced his engagement, those who had known Christopher and Nancy over the previous seven years were delighted by their marriage and many of them attended their wedding in June 1990.

Later, when I got to know Spence a little better, I discovered that he was under no illusion about what people thought of him. 'It looks as if I'm very impulsive,' he said, 'but in fact I'm extraordinarily patient until, that is, there comes a point when I get exasperated and have to act. For some people who haven't been immediately involved in the process, it'll look like a frightfully rough zooming-in intervention but they don't realise I've spent months trying to get action.'

He pointed out to me that he had had a lot to learn when he first started running Lighthouse because he hadn't worked in an organisation for over twenty years which was possibly why some people criticised his managerial approach as being tough and heavy-handed. He understood why he was a highly controversial figure. 'I'm the founder of Lighthouse, I have a very strong personality. I'm also older than most people here and on top of that I'm a white upper-middle class married man who happens also to be gay. All that put together, plus the fact that I'm an authority figure, is very hard for people to swallow.'

Equally, there were just as many people at Lighthouse who found him an inspirational leader figure. Although I personally never had any very close dealings with him, I always felt a warmth when with him. Some people may have felt intimidated by his decisive and energetic presence but if you could overcome that initial sense of awesome respect, beneath the surface lay an extremely approachable, supportive and sensitive human being. While some staff may have complained about him, the majority obviously felt a great loyalty towards him, and when the *Independent on Sunday* published a stinging attack on his autocratic style of leadership, a great many wrote to the newspaper in protest, stating their pride in the organisation and describing Spence as 'untraditionally accessible, understanding and open to ideas'.

Spence's style of management was for some people epitomised in the way he dealt with the ailing cafe. Ever since my arrival at Lighthouse there had been discontent in the way the cafe was run and in the declining quality of the food. There was talk of wastage, financial loss and a dissatisfied workforce.

When one day in the late summer, staff and service users arrived at Lighthouse to find a memo from Spence pinned to the front door announcing the closure of the cafe until further notice, many were shocked by what appeared to be such sudden and drastic action. The crucial facts, however, were that in addition to the heavy losses (which were eventually accounted for) Lighthouse was failing both in its only statutory obligation to provide an adequate standard of food for residents, as well as in meeting the requirements of the Food Safety Act. In fact, the kitchen had become a serious health hazard and could easily have been closed down altogether had the Environmental Health Officer been aware of the state of affairs. Later, at the 1991 Annual Conference, Spence explained his reasons for closing the cafe: 'We felt we were digging ourselves deeper and deeper into deficit and the first step was to stop digging and to consider carefully our options.'

With the closure of the cafe, a light went out at Lighthouse and people were at great pains to express its importance as a focal point of the organisation. For some service users it was the only place where they could get a cheap, hot meal; for paid and unpaid staff it was a place where they could have a break whilst still being on hand if required; for residents it provided a welcome alternative to the sometimes hothouse atmosphere of the unit; and for the local community it was the only part of the organisation which they could enter with ease and which allowed them to share in the life of London Lighthouse.

Thankfully, several weeks after its closure the cafe opened again under a new more experienced manager and Lighthouse's pulse started to beat again.

· *Six* ·

Although I would not claim to have ever been particularly proficient or indeed very involved in the care of my brother who had Muscular Dystrophy, the world of sickness was familiar terrain to me and I found it hard to understand some people's fear and revulsion of AIDS. I could not make out if it was contagion they feared or proximity to the chronically ill.

Before I started working as a volunteer I thought of AIDS as a long drawn out and mostly fatal illness and I imagined that I would be working with very sick people indeed. But the reality proved different – many of the people whom I came to know were still asymptomatic and perfectly well. Though statistically the outlook for people with HIV was bleak, with most doctors forecasting that a vast majority of people with HIV would go on to develop full-blown AIDS, there was not the sense of despair and inevitability at London Lighthouse that I had expected. In fact, there was sometimes even a surprising mood of optimism since people were living longer, more productive lives. Longevity was not seen as the desired ideal we have all been brought up to assume is our right. Quality rather than quantity was what counted. Your attitude towards time therefore became a very important factor in living well with AIDS. Months seemed more like years, and years more like decades in the sense that people took short cuts, did things they might never have otherwise done, formed close friendships which under different circumstances would have taken years to establish, and started to edit the content of their lives in such a way that there was enough time and space for the things that really mattered.

Until I started working at Lighthouse I had not realised the extent of the ignorance and fear that still surrounded AIDS and the question of its transmission. I was surprised and saddened by the number of my friends and acquaintances – all supposedly well-informed, liberal people – who asked me if I was worried about putting my own health at risk and if it was advisable to allow my daughter to be touched by people at Lighthouse.

I had to explain again and again that HIV was a virus which could be transmitted only in three specific ways – by blood, from mother to child *in utero* and by the exchange of body fluids in penetrative sexual activity. Infection through casual or even close bodily contact was not considered possible since the virus, existing inside a tough rubbery coating, was extremely fragile and lived only momentarily outside body fluids. The virus was known to be transmitted through blood, semen, vaginal fluids (and very rarely through breast milk); it was present in, but not transmitted through, saliva, tears and sweat; and had never been found in faeces, urine or vomit.

But I understood their fear too. The husband of an old friend admitted to me that he felt guilty and upset about not wanting a close friend from Canada to come and stay who had recently been diagnosed as having AIDS because he feared for the safety of his two young daughters. Even though I tried to explain to him why there was no risk to his children, he wasn't satisfied with my explanation and only repeated what his GP had told him – namely that the medical profession knew frighteningly little about this virus since it was changing all the time.

Staff at Lighthouse frequently had to deal with queries from the public which demonstrated a profound lack of awareness about AIDS and how it was transmitted. One evening when I was working late a woman rang to ask if it was all right for her to drive the car of someone who had AIDS. She was worried that she might catch it from touching the keys or the steering wheel and that her child was even more at risk than she was. On another occasion a man came in and said he'd been having a drink with a man in a pub who he thought had AIDS. The man had bought him a drink and handed him the glass. He was worried that this innocent transaction could somehow have infected him.

Everyone who worked at Lighthouse had experienced this sort of ignorance from members of the public. Some people even showed open hostility. Carol told me how the man who came to fix her boiler put down the cup of tea that he'd been drinking when she happened to mention that she worked for an AIDS charity and he refused to touch another drop.

Sometimes even friends and family could have disappointing reactions. Caroline, another Lighthouse worker, told me she had experienced a lot of fear and ignorance among her friends: 'Most of them are so frightened about AIDS, they don't want to talk about it. In a way it's a relief because I don't want to be a teacher when I get home as well as when I'm at work, but on the other hand I'd rather they asked than made assumptions about HIV. Most of my friends are lesbians and you'd think they'd be more clued up than most, but they're not. There's a real ostrich mentality among the lesbian community.'

Even among gay men there were those who were remarkably ignorant. One member of staff talked about having been to a party of what he described as 'A-gays' – in other words wealthy antique dealers who lived in large houses on the river and who, despite being educated and cosmopolitan, had never heard of London Lighthouse. This particular member of staff was shocked and infuriated by such an evasion of responsibility and would tell them firmly where to send their money.

Even gay men who were well-informed sometimes didn't want to know. A close friend of mine, whom I had known for many years and who had a reasonable chance of having the virus, didn't want to have the test and wouldn't read anything about AIDS. He used to ask me how my work was going at Lighthouse but he didn't really want to hear the answer. He was aware he had this tendency and saw it as a weakness but knew that it was his only way of coping with the threat of AIDS. Denial, I soon realised, was prevalent – among those who had tested positive, among those who didn't want to have the test, and even among those who had tested negative. One male nurse told me that a lot of his gay friends flatly refused to talk about his work because they themselves were at risk and believed that if they didn't think about the problem, somehow it would go away.

While I was working on reception I got to know a volunteer who had the virus. His name was Liam and he told me how he had been having a relationship for a year with a man who knew he worked at Lighthouse but didn't know he was HIV-positive because he was so extremely adept at avoiding the subject. They practised safer sex so Liam trusted he wasn't putting his lover at risk but the burden of his hidden secret had begun to weigh heavily on his conscience. We spoke often about the problem. Liam desperately wanted to tell his partner and was always looking for an opportune moment in which to do so but that moment never seemed to come because every time Liam made a determination to bring up the subject, his lover would become withdrawn and taciturn. Once he refused to kiss Liam because Liam had just told him how he'd spent the day sitting with a man who was dying of AIDS. He would hide away any London Lighthouse leaflets or correspondence, and he never asked Liam about his work.

Only once did he voluntarily bring up the subject of AIDS when he got a letter from a Dutch friend telling him that he had just been diagnosed HIV positive. Liam tried to pursue the subject but his friend snarled back ferociously, 'Let's not talk about this now!' Liam said, 'It was like having a door opened slightly and then slammed tightly in your face.' He was convinced that if his lover found out about his HIV status he would leave him, but I was not so sure. It seemed logical to assume that anyone working in an AIDS organisation might have the virus and, since Liam's lover was no fool, he must have been aware of that possibility.

Liam's counsellor had frequently tried to help him find the courage to tell his partner that he was positive and face the consequences. I always suspected that deep down this man knew or rather suspected Liam's status but thought that by not mentioning it it would cease to be an issue. I later found out that the relationship came to an abrupt end soon after (ostensibly for other more superficial reasons) and without the subject of HIV ever having come up again. Liam didn't feel guilty about this, he had never had penetrative sex with his partner and felt he had tried as hard as he could to make him face the facts so it was not his fault that he had continuously come up against a brick wall.

Brad – whom I met on my induction course – had a similar problem though in his case there had never been any attempt to hide from his lover the fact that he was HIV positive. However, his lover hated talking about it and was extremely skilful at avoiding the topic. Brad's mother was also living in a state of denial. She had recently been widowed and left a substantial sum of money by her husband which was to be shared out among her children after her death. Brad was in the process of trying to explain to his mother that he would be dead long before she ever was and that a small amount of the money would come in very handy now in order to secure a roof over his head and pay for nursing care should he become too ill to look after himself. But his mother refused to accept that her son would die before she did.

'Both my parents were very good at accepting the fact that I was gay,' Brad said, 'but they never wanted to talk about HIV. Before my father died and before I knew for sure I was positive I tried to involve him in arranging some insurance for me but he accused me of being a hypochondriac. Now my lover refuses to let AIDS play any part in his life. He's never sat at anyone's bedside and never seen any of his friends get sick and die. When I talk about my fear of the future he thinks I'm being gloomy and tries to change the subject. I'm sure this is partly because he wants to cheer me up but he doesn't realise that talking about it is one of the ways that I deal with it and I need that outlet. So even though he doesn't encourage it I talk to him about my illness all the same. I tell him about everything whether he's listening or not. I tell him about what medication I'm on, how my T-cell count is doing, and what my counsellor has said. He hardly ever responds but at least it's a way of getting it out of my system.'

On the induction course Brad stood out from the rest of us because he was American and because he spoke with ease and fluency about himself and about AIDS. He was the only person who in introducing himself revealed that he was HIV positive and I was intrigued when later he told me that he had known Harvey Milk, the gay American activist, murdered in 1978 and who for a long time had held a great fascination for me.

Over the course of my time at Lighthouse I learnt a lot about Brad. He had grown up in New England and come out in the early seventies at the age of sixteen.

'I was a wimpy, intellectual, Jewish boy and in American culture if you're not a real jock you're gay. I always knew I was gay but I didn't have enough sense to stay in the closet. I think people who don't discover they're gay until they're thirty or forty are better off than people who come out in their twenties – because they seem to be socialised in a more conventional way and are more directed in their career.'

He ran off with another boy at seventeen but this person turned out to be a violent alcoholic, and Brad found it hard to handle. When his friend didn't return at night, he became hysterical. He had always romantically fantasised about being married – in other words having a monogamous relationship with a man which would last for many years.

In 1968 he came to England with a tiny allowance given to him by his parents. 'I had no sex at all at that time. I never cruised toilets because I didn't know how it was done and I hated gay bars which were full of drag queens and people being evil to each other. Instead I joined the hippy culture which suited me fine because no one minded who I was or what I looked like. For about five years I had barely any contact with gay men, because even hippies at that time were very repressed.

Then one day I saw an ad in one of the underground papers from someone who professed to being a gay hippy fed up with the materialistic gay culture and who wanted to know if there were any other gay hippies around. So I wrote back immediately and thirty of us got together at the London School of Economics. It was an electric meeting which turned out to be the very beginnings of the Gay Liberation Front. We'd experienced tolerance but now we were demanding acceptance.' At first the gay scene seemed very liberating. Brad became involved in street theatre and in producing a gay newspaper. It was a time of intense discussion when people came out in droves.

Eventually, however, he returned to America and went to live in California where he remained for fifteen years. He had grown up experiencing American prudery but now it seemed that America was much more liberal than England. 'At first I had trouble being sexually open. The bath houses were purpose built and big business in the seventies and I thought they were really shocking. You could cruise anywhere – in supermarkets, launderettes or in parks.

'I lived in the Castro district just as it was becoming the popular gay area and I became a bar tender at the most prestigious gay bar in town. It was a wonderful experience: I made lots of money and everyone knew me. San Francisco must be the only place in the world where a bar tender is a celebrity. At the same time I got involved in a gay liberation newspaper and got to know Harvey Milk who had a camera shop up the road. We were both gay Jews who never really fitted in.

'But I was disillusioned with the gay culture. I had thought being gay meant going to the ballet and reading Proust, whereas most gays in the Castro came from the Midwest, liked listening to Country and Western music and going bowling. No one would come to the ballet with me because it was too feminine. I was disappointed in the way gay people lived. I saw a lot of gay men using each other because when it came down to it they were only interested in who had the strongest body and the biggest dick. I felt very used, and was stood up at least two hundred times, even though I never stood up anyone myself. I felt deeply let down by my community. I expected gay people to be better than other people but they weren't.'

Then in 1980 Brad read the first reports of how several gay men in Los Angeles had a rare skin cancer called Kaposi's Sarcoma (KS) which was baffling the medical establishment. He was in the process of splitting up with a boyfriend at the time and was looking forward to relaxing into a new sexual freedom, but this ominous news sounded a warning bell. 'That same year I had a dream about the gay parade. I had religiously gone on the parade every year but this was the first time I was considering giving it a miss. I dreamt I went down to the civic centre to join the parade when I discovered that a bomb had gone off, so I ran south in order to avoid the crowds because I was so scared. Even in my dream I realised the significance of this. The movement had become empty for me and gay life was exploding in front of my eyes.'

By 1982 Brad was following the progress of AIDS intensely, having realised that he could no longer behave exactly as he pleased. If a cure was to be found for the disease, it wouldn't be for at least twenty years and by then all the fun would be over for him. Soon he began knowing people who were sick, although at first they tended to be people he didn't know well. 'Nor did I respect them much. It looked as if the most promiscuous were dying first, so I stopped being as promiscuous as I had been and began to imagine that I might be spared. I had had sex with strangers but not many. On the other hand I liked being fucked and the word was that passive partners were the ones most at risk. I got very depressed when I realised this because at that time it seemed to me that life wasn't worth living without sex.

'The first person I knew who died was a hairdresser and a famous party-giver in the Castro. I had slept with him only once. He would invite hundreds of men to his parties which I never enjoyed because a room full of hundreds of exposed chests was not my idea of fun. I found it hard to feel any sympathy for him when he died. Then a bar tender, who I'd also slept with and who had also treated me like shit, died. I went to his funeral but they couldn't find six pall bearers to carry the coffin even though he'd supposedly had hundreds of friends. I felt very angry with them, but also guilty about my reaction to their deaths. Guys were dying who had lied and stood me up and I couldn't even muster up an ounce of sympathy.

'I had the test in 1986. By then I'd made the assumption that I was positive so when the doctor confirmed it, although I was shocked it was no surprise to me and besides I still felt there was an escape route. At that time they didn't necessarily think being HIV positive led to AIDS whereas I have since read that the only co-factor is time. I felt angry too because I had given so much to the gay liberation movement and in return had been stood up hundreds of times, and had finally been infected by the HIV virus. I felt angry with the authorities too. If the right epidemiological research had been done early enough then at least we'd have reached the common consensus earlier that it's important to use a rubber. But, in a perverse sort of way, I also felt pleased to be HIV positive because I've never wanted to be left out of things and this meant that I was one of the crowd.

'In some ways I saw AIDS as a positive thing. It created a second generation of gay men who were more caring and community-involved and it resulted in a slowing down of the commercial aspect of San Francisco. I've always believed in recreational sex, but I don't believe in men being used for sex and treated like objects. Promiscuity has its roots in oppression. If your initial experience of sex is in a toilet then you carry on that way because you can't get excited unless you're in a toilet or somewhere that looks very like a toilet. I'm a middle-class gay American and I can't bear those places. The bath houses in San Francisco have since been closed down but they still exist in L.A. and Munich, although only oral sex is allowed now and they are self-policed by moderators who go into the steam rooms to make sure that there's no fucking going on.

'I've noticed a certain prudery among some gay men these days. I've met gay men who won't have oral sex unless they're wearing three layers of plastic. But, at the same time, new conventions have struck up and there are also those who don't use any protection at all. I was once in a cab in Paris with two American men who I'd never met before. I told them immediately that I was HIV positive, to which one of them replied: "Who isn't?" We didn't use rubbers because there was no penetrative sex but no one seemed concerned about AIDS.'

Because he was asymptomatic for so long, Brad, like so many others in his position, felt for a long time he was somehow magically protected from developing full-blown AIDS. Even when he started getting a few symptoms, he still felt it wasn't touching him the way it was touching other people, especially since most of what was wrong with him seemed to have been caused by doctors or by drugs rather than by the virus itself. But then, early in 1991, he was taken to hospital with a fever and was diagnosed as having PCP pneumonia.

'I've never been told by a doctor that I have AIDS, although it must be written down somewhere. I had no problem saying I was HIV positive because I was asymptomatic then but it's very difficult for me to say I've got AIDS. I know I'm still denying a lot. I see emaciated people and I think I'm never going to be one of them. I spend my life waiting for something to happen. I keep telling myself "take courage". I don't mind dying that much but I do mind getting very sick and becoming a burden on people.'

Brad vanished from Lighthouse not long after he had started working there as a volunteer. I never managed to trace him again, and I suspect he may have returned to the States since he was becoming increasingly dissatisfied with his life in the UK. Although he had spoken highly of Lighthouse as one of the few places in England where he felt free to speak and act without censure, he never became very involved in the organisation and I sensed that things hadn't gone quite the way he'd hoped or anticipated. Equally, his health was failing and he may well have felt the need to distance himself from a world he so loathed having to inhabit. He had always been adamant that he didn't want to work on the residential unit. He once told me: 'I've known so many people who have died of AIDS and in a superstitious sort of way I don't want to drag the illness into my life more than it is already.'

· *Seven* ·

Some of the service users wandering through the reception area were using Daycare facilities. As in other parts of London Lighthouse, the philosophy of Daycare was about control and dignity, advocacy and autonomy, even though there was growing recognition that in the case of HIV dementia there was a limit to the amount of control people could have over their lives.

Although not everyone attending Daycare had psychological problems, the majority had either HIV-related dementia, reactive depression or mental problems. Because people were living longer with AIDS (due to more accurate diagnosis, better drug treatment and improved acute care facilities) neurological symptoms were now increasing. In the early days, very few people with AIDS lived long enough to suffer from dementia whereas now it was affecting an estimated 40 per cent. From autopsy results, it appeared that 80 per cent of people who had died from AIDS had some sort of central nervous system damage although there may never have been any evidence of this during their lifetime.

Confusion and dementia could either be organic (neurological) or functional (psychological); it was not always possible to tell what was causing it other than through diagnostic tests. These people were sometimes completely unaware of what was happening to them or they might be very aware and consequently very tormented – but usually it was a bit of both with people having some degree of insight some of the time. Dementia could bring out certain characteristics in a person that had always been there though they were mostly hidden, and mood swings were common. A personality change could be total so that the very essence of that person was missing, or it could be minimal so that only someone who knew that person well would have been able to recognise the changes. Difficulties with co-ordination and mobility were also common. At its worst HIV-related dementia meant that someone had very little mobility, total disinhibition, apathy, morbidity and an inability to communicate.

I became increasingly adept at identifying dementia. For instance there was Quentin whose manner and tone of voice was unnaturally precise and pedantic. He had been a teacher but was now suffering from severe memory loss – both long- and short-term. He was obsessive about detail because it was his only way of keeping a grip on reality but he frequently lost hold of this grip and could then be seen pacing corridors and muttering angrily to himself in a state of deep confusion. His memory loss was so bad that I don't believe he had a great deal of insight into his condition.

For Beatrice it was worse. She was a mother and a former Law Centre worker who had been forced to give up both her job and her child due to her deteriorating condition. In the case of her job she could no longer remember facts and in the case of her daughter she wanted her to start a fresh life with her father in Ireland. She was in anguish, not only because she'd lost the person she loved most, but also because it appeared she was beginning to suffer from a degree of HIV-related dementia and was painfully aware of this fact.

One day she came up to me at reception in tears because she'd locked her keys in the car with the engine still running. It was something any of us could have done but in Beatrice's case it came on top of a number of other incidents all of which were clear indications that her brain was not functioning as well as it once had been. She was very agitated and although the keys were eventually retrieved, for the rest of the day she could be seen wandering around the building looking sad and dejected.

For her, like for so many others, London Lighthouse was a refuge. It was a place to go where she could meet friends, build a routine to her life, and receive practical and emotional support. Though Lighthouse may not always have succeeded in changing the attitude of people with AIDS so that they started leading more positive and meaningful lives, it certainly succeeded in improving the quality of a great many people's lives by providing them with a safe space where they could be themselves, develop new relationships and prepare for their future. Some people I met would undoubtedly have led far more isolated and lonely lives if Lighthouse had not existed and for their partners and families too the burden of responsibility would have been far more awesome.

Unruly and antisocial behaviour didn't necessarily mean that someone was suffering from dementia, and as a volunteer I had constantly to reconsider my own judgements of people's behaviour. There was one occasion, early on during my time at Lighthouse, when I got talking to a man who had used Lighthouse services for many months. Pierre was a French man in his early forties who had come to England in 1978 in order to live in a country which he felt was more accepting of gay men. His benign and sociable demeanour meant that he was much liked at Lighthouse by both staff and service users.

Despite his openness, I remember feeling awkward when I first met Pierre and I note with shame that I wrote in my diary at that time: 'Of all the people who I've talked to at Lighthouse Pierre has been the least forthcoming. There is something a little bit shifty and strange about him.' Later, when I understood more about HIV-related dementia and memory loss, I realised that what I took for shiftiness was not that at all, but simply a reflection of the struggle taking place within his mind to separate illusion from reality.

Pierre, I discovered, had been suffering mildly from AIDS-related dementia for many months but in May 1991 his condition began to deteriorate rapidly. It was difficult to estimate how much he understood about the process taking place within his mind as sometimes he would appear to be very lucid and clear-headed while at other times he would suddenly slip into a state of confusion whereby he would lose thread of what he was saying and suddenly become distracted and monosyllabic. It was like watching someone's thought processes slow down as the batteries began to wear out.

Pierre was rarely angry which made me think that he probably had only occasional glimpses into his own condition. For the most part he lived in the world of denial, refusing to accept his AIDS diagnosis, filling in endless job applications and planning holidays abroad. Towards the end of his life it was tragic to see how someone who had obviously once been an extremely able man, both mentally and physically, slowly ceased to be able to look after himself. Even a most simple task, like brushing his teeth, became a long drawn-out and painful process since he no longer had the cognitive ability to finish what he had started. At the same time his sleep patterns became very disturbed and he lost all awareness of when people normally go to bed and get up. He wore an expensive Rolex watch which was in fact of very little use to him since he could no longer tell the time.

When Pierre became too demented to look after himself, his friends devised a rota to ensure that he had someone with him for twenty-four hours of the day. To give them some respite he attended Daycare at Lighthouse at least three days a week. This was, they said, the only safe and accepting environment they had found for him outside his own home. One of Pierre's main supports was a retired nurse who told me that, as the carer of someone with AIDS-related dementia, her main objective was to maintain Pierre's safety. For her, dementia was a living bereavement. 'You're dead before you've actually died,' she said. 'It's a terrible thing because it strips you of so much, preventing you from functioning normally in life.'

She told me that as a carer it was very difficult to find a degree of care which would maintain Pierre's dignity and safety, while at the same time would not collude with his deluded state. She added, however, that if that deluded state was a perfectly safe state to be in, then it was important to acknowledge and not to deny it. She had frequently been with Pierre on journeys into his past and although these might have taken place twenty times in the space of one hour, if they were doing no harm, she would never try to break the delusion. Similarly she would help him plan holidays and fill out job applications. 'It's so important to accept and expect emotional fluctuations and frustrations,' she told me. I realised it took a certain sort of person to look after someone with cognitive impairment. Not only did you need to be specially trained but you needed infinite patience which somehow I doubted I had.

I later learnt that Pierre died in the summer of 1992. In some respects he was fortunate to have had so many good friends supporting and loving him up until the end, plus the care and expertise of people at Lighthouse who were trained to look after people with AIDS-related dementia. Many in the same position were not so lucky since society generally finds personality and behavioural disorders harder to accept than physical impairment which may ultimately kill but at least leaves the brain intact.

While I was working at reception I saw many people come into the building distressed, shocked, and bewildered – many of whom had received a recent diagnosis and were suffering from post-test reaction. Diagnosis was almost always accompanied by shock with a person becoming very inward-looking as a form of self-protection.

Sadly I saw many people seeking counselling at Lighthouse and being turned away because the counselling department was fully booked and unable to take on any new referrals. However, once the new drop-in support service became available in the summer of 1991, it guaranteed that there would always be someone available to talk to at Lighthouse. This was a service run by trained volunteers, who worked in shifts and offered a listening ear to anyone who walked through the door.

Robin was a typical service user who came through the doors shortly after Lighthouse first opened and who died in the winter of 1991. He lived with his partner in Wimbledon and had been told about Lighthouse by a friend's partner who had stayed on the residential unit. Robin told me he had been in a state of complete disbelief and shock when he first came to Lighthouse. It was three o'clock in the afternoon and he had only received the result of his test that morning.

He came back every week for a few months after that to see one of the counsellors and then he disappeared for a while. A few months later he returned for some more sessions, as did his partner. He also came to use some of the other services such as Day Care and the complementary therapies. I got to know him several months after our initial meeting when he came for a brief stay on the residential unit. He was a very curious person and always wanted to know a lot about me although he was never very keen to talk about himself. The one thing he would enthuse about was how incredibly important Lighthouse had become to him and he spoke very warmly of his counsellor who had seen him at his lowest point and helped put him back on course.

'When I first saw my counsellor, I was told that I was reacting in a normal way to an abnormal situation. It helped to be told that what I was feeling was the body and mind's natural reaction to something which was very difficult to handle, and to be reassured that this feeling wouldn't last for ever. I was bombarded with information and although I only took in about half of what was being said to me, it helped because I began to understand the process I was going through and the reasons why I had become so disfunctional. I remember feeling at the time that the very essence of my life was soiled and I really thought I'd be better off dead.'

Many people experienced this sort of reaction. One of the counsellors told me that contamination was a key word in counselling, and that often people felt they couldn't have sex because they felt so unclean. I even heard of one woman who said she wanted to get hold of a brillo pad to clean her insides out.

London Lighthouse didn't offer pre-test counselling because there were other places which existed especially for that, so those who used the counselling service were either living with the virus or their lives were in some way affected by it. Much of the work was crisis intervention. Someone could turn up in a highly charged emotional state unable to make sense of what had happened to them. They might be tearful, suicidal or unable to speak from the shock of having their world turned upside-down and inside-out and a counsellor would give them space to scream, cry and get rid of some of their pent-up emotion or, if they were paralysed with fear, just let them know that someone was available to listen when the time was right. There were no learned techniques to make someone talk, the important thing was to sit with them and make them feel safe so that they wanted to talk. Crisis intervention was sometimes necessary in other situations as well, such as when someone with HIV started to develop symptoms, or when someone's lover died of AIDS, or when a mother discovered that her son was not only gay but had AIDS as well.

Not everyone wanted to see a counsellor and, of those that did, not all actually needed to. Some just wanted a bit of companionship and advice and, although clients were never turned away, counsellors hoped that these people would realise themselves that they'd be better off seeking a different kind of support. Also there were those for whom the only way of getting over their anxiety about AIDS was to talk it to death in the hope that there was a therapeutic answer. Similarly other people thought the only way of surviving was to stay mentally alert and by going to all the groups, reading all the books, and attending all the meetings. But often all this succeeded in doing was to make everything seem like an enormous effort and burden. It encouraged paranoia, too, because it could potentially lead to the belief that 'no one understands me outside the world of HIV' and this would ultimately lead to isolation and exclusion from the real world.

Different people needed different things from counselling. Some people needed to express the emotions they'd been burying while other people needed tightening up, so that if, for example, they were being very emotional all of the time, they needed to look at other ways of dealing with what was going on inside. Crying and getting angry had its place but too much of it could be unhelpful.

Sometimes making people aware of something wasn't enough, and counsellors had to look at the way their client saw the world and processed information. This meant working with what people brought with them – in some cases being intrusive and in other cases holding back. Counsellors enabled people to make sense of events for themselves. It was a way of opening the floodgates and releasing the pressure that had built up inside. Once this had happened someone could develop an insight into themselves, identify strengths and become familiar with the resources they had to draw on. One counsellor told me he would never give false reassurance. 'I'll never tell someone that I'm sure it will get better soon, because it probably won't: the most honest response I can give is that I hope things will get better soon,' he said.

Much of what the counselling department did was known as normalising work – in other words trying to get people to lead a normal life. One counsellor told me: 'It's not a matter of getting them to do something against their will because I let them arrive at their own decisions. I may think something but I won't ever say it, I just try to lead them in that direction and if they don't want to go then I'll leave it and go in another direction. It's simply a matter of shifting the goals.'

To give an example of this, he told me about a client of his who had been under the spell of a very promiscuous lover who lived in the South of France. He had been working with this man for two years helping him disentangle himself from what was a very unsatisfactory and one-sided relationship. It was a process of helping him find his true identity. To start with the counselling had been a success to the extent that his client had abandoned his feminine demeanour (handbags, nail varnish, mascara etc.) which he had never felt happy with but had adopted at the request of his lover. But then everything changed because his lover began to be nice again and demanded he revert to his feminine appearance.

One counsellor told me she didn't raise the issue about changing sexual practices unless she was talking to someone who was extremely active – for example having something in the region of a hundred partners a month, which was now extremely unusual. She insisted that there was no advantage in bringing it up in a punitive sense and experience had shown her that, over a period of counselling, sexually active gay men usually eased off without ever having to address the issue directly.

Passive partners were considered to be at greater risk of infection than active partners, although they were less likely to infect others. Brad, who told me that he only liked 'bottoms', believed this slightly absolved him of the moral dilemma of whether to tell people or not. 'I usually say to men, I'm probably positive, so if you want to wear a rubber it's up to you, but I always ask them to pull out if they're going to come. No one tells you that safer sex is not nearly as nice as unprotected sex and sometimes I feel like behaving like a little boy: I want to stamp my foot and say I don't care anymore because 95 per cent of the time my partners have treated me shittily, and why should I be bothered to go to all this effort to protect them, when basically they don't give a damn. I've been tempted to think it's their responsibility and not to mention my HIV status but my conscience always gets the better of me.'

Philip Sanderson (the then group head of Residential Services) confessed to me that for him the issue around safe sex had taken a long time to sink in. Like many gay men diagnosed with HIV, he felt betrayed by his own kind, and for six months after the diagnosis he was more promiscuous than he had been at any time in his life. 'I didn't give a damn,' he told me. 'If they didn't ask about protecting themselves I wouldn't bother. It was my way of getting back at the person who had given it to me.'

This was a reaction I heard repeated many times, even to the extent that one man I met had dealt with his lover's death wholly inappropriately by going out and becoming a male prostitute.

I came to realise that feelings of revenge and bitterness were not uncommon. Several of the people I got to know admitted that immediately after diagnosis they hadn't had protected sex and still occasionally omitted wearing a condom. Some had become much more promiscuous since being diagnosed HIV positive, because having unsafe sex was as in Philip's case their way of getting back at the person who had infected them with HIV.

Another Lighthouse employee told me that for a long time he didn't change his lifestyle because he believed it was other people's responsibility to ask for safer sex. It was only when he stopped taking recreational drugs that he was able to think more clearly and see that it was his responsibility to have safer sex. 'I stopped taking Ecstasy and acid on Saturday nights because that was what made my T-cell count go down to 124. I would get tired after dancing for five minutes when previously I'd been able to carry on until 5 a.m. Now I don't go to clubs at all anymore and I don't miss them,' he told me. 'As a result I've lost all my old friends who were obviously only interested in me because I could get hold of drugs, but I've replaced them with some new, and much more valuable friendships.' As someone who was still very much in touch with what was happening on the gay scene, he was insistent that there hadn't been the change of behaviour people talked of. He said there were still many people practising unsafe sex and having multiple partners.

He was probably right, although the pubs and clubs he once frequented would have attracted only one section of the community. By the early 1990s, however, evidence of increasing anal gonorrhoea among homosexual men seemed to suggest that active partners were not using condoms as much as they had done in the early days of the disease. Several people told me that in their experience one very worrying factor seemed to be coming to light, namely that young men coming on to the scene were of the firm belief that AIDS was a problem that belonged only to the previous generation.

Post-test counselling was about exploring what it means to be positive and looking at the difference between HIV and AIDS. The issues would change according to the individuals concerned and according to how well they had processed the information.

For instance, it took many months of gentle persuasion on Beatrice's part to get her partner, Gerry, to see a counsellor at Lighthouse. She wanted him to be able to discuss the next stages of her disease with someone in a supportive and rational way.

'One reason I wanted him to see a counsellor,' she said, 'was because it was difficult to know what was appropriate for us to talk about. I was getting fed up hearing all the time about his fear of me dying. I felt it was very important for him to talk to a counsellor so that he could come to grips with what was going on and look at the changing dynamics of our relationship. For example, when we first got together I was the one who was in a state and he was the one who was denying that anything was wrong. Now I seem to have got my life sorted out and can actually envisage a future for myself whereas he's in a state of panic, not least because he was made redundant last month. In other words he's now having to adjust to being a full-time carer, instead of being a wage earner and it's tough. Also, we find it difficult to be as physically close as we used to be. It feels as if there's a wedge in our relationship because neither of us wants to do anything that will harm my health.'

Beatrice did not see a counsellor for herself. She felt she got all the support she needed from talking to her friends and her family. Gerry, on the other hand, was far more emotionally withdrawn than she was and felt it was a sign of failure to rely on friends for support. For the short while he received counselling Beatrice said he discovered things about himself which he had hitherto been completely unaware of.

Inevitably, other issues came up during counselling which had nothing to do with being HIV positive, for instance problems to do with relationships, careers or unresolved issues of grief and loss in childhood; increasingly it was as if HIV was becoming less and less the issue.

Incredible as it may seem, it was possible to put your HIV status out of sight and out of mind. I met several people who told me that, after the initial shock of diagnosis when they found themselves inhabiting a nightmare world of fear and unreality, a new calm set in. Robin was one of these. Within a few weeks he had adjusted to the fact that he was HIV positive and for several months disappeared from Lighthouse altogether, because he felt he no longer needed its services, although perhaps also unconsciously because Lighthouse reminded him of all those things he had managed so successfully to suppress. Later he discovered that there were matters to do with death and dying which he still needed to look at.

This was how he described to me the stages he went through: 'The first stage was waking up in the morning and praying that I was still asleep because the knowledge that I would develop AIDS was just too much to bear. Then a horrible sickening feeling would spread across my body as I realised that this indeed was my reality and so I would sink back into bed, unable to get up and face another day with the virus. The second stage was waking up and being able to accept immediately and calmly that I was HIV positive, and being able to get up, put on my suit and go to work just as I'd always done. I could concentrate on reading my newspaper again and for fleeting moments even forget that I was positive. The next stage was stopping thinking about my status altogether. I could forget about it for days on end. I was living my life just as before, I was still working, still having sex, and still making decisions for myself.' The final stage that Robin could identify was realising that there were areas of conflict and concern that needed to be looked at both on his part and the part of his partner and family, in particular his mother. Although he would have preferred to stick his head in the sand, he had enough self-awareness to know that burying problems was unlikely to make them go away.

This period of denial was common with most people who had the virus. Living every minute of the day with the knowledge of a potentially fatal illness is not humanly possible, so everyone needs periods of denial. The normal process of human reaction to terminal illness, identified by Elizabeth Kubler-Ross in her work on death and the dying, is shock, denial, bargaining, depression and finally acceptance. Not everyone goes through all these stages, nor necessarily in that order, and some never reach the final stage of acceptance.

With AIDS, denial came in the form of distancing yourself from your status and the world of HIV as Robin had done or like a woman I met who was dying of lymphoma but refused to make a will because she didn't think she needed to. There was undoubtedly a place for denial but too much of it left a person feeling confused and worried as if walking up a blind alley. Only working with the fear enabled someone to carry on with living.

After Robin's death I got to know his partner Steve and was struck by his honesty, his willingness to show his vulnerability and to admit to mistakes and weaknesses. Steve had already known Robin for three years when he was diagnosed HIV positive. Because he had been just as sexually active as his lover, he was certain that he too would test positive. However, he was wrong.

'I didn't exactly leap in the air and shout with joy when they told me I was negative. In fact, my first reaction was that life was terribly, terribly unfair and my second reaction was that I had to stand by Robin no matter what because that's why I'd been let off the hook. Our relationship had been pretty up and down until then and I'm not sure if it would have lasted had it not been for AIDS. I'll never forget having to tell Robin my test result. Part of me felt extremely relieved because I hadn't been given a death sentence, but the other half felt extremely guilty because Robin had. It seemed as random as that. I cried my eyes out and Robin comforted me.'

After Robin's diagnosis Steve moved in with him, not because he needed any care at that stage but because he felt it was a sign of solidarity and showed he meant to stick the course. A year later Robin gave up his job as a landscape gardener to concentrate on preserving his health and from then on Steve managed to support them both from his own catering business.

'I know I wasn't very good with Robin at the beginning,' he told me. 'I said it would make no difference to our relationship but of course it did. For instance, it instantly changed my sexual feelings towards him. I couldn't help it. Even if we had the very safest sex, using three rubbers and all the creams in the world, I would feel restricted and worried. The only way we got over this was by talking about it. Thankfully, Robin was very understanding and I think his sexual appetite had anyway already diminished. In the end with the help of a bit of counselling and relaxing we found there were things we could do which were enjoyable for both of us and which didn't make me anxious or inhibited.

'Because Robin was fairly well for eighteen months, only very occasionally getting symptoms such as swollen glands and night sweats, and because I'm pretty good at putting things to the back of my mind, to start with I managed not to think about HIV. I thought it would be healthier for both of us if we didn't talk about it too much. Robin abided by these unspoken rules but it came out later that he found my attitude very unhelpful. He said that for the first four or five months he didn't think about AIDS in either a negative or a positive way but as his body began to change and he got rashes and sore eyes and felt nauseous much of the time, he realised that there was a metamorphosis taking place which had started internally and was now beginning to manifest itself externally. I hadn't appreciated this nor did I realise how terribly tired he felt all the time. The exhaustion alone was enough to mean that for him his HIV status was in his mind every minute of every waking hour.'

It was only when Robin developed PCP and was given an AIDS diagnosis that Steve faced the reality of what lay ahead, and with no experience of chronic illness, he suddenly panicked. Reading up about AIDS and talking to more and more people who either had the virus themselves or cared for someone who did, it began to dawn on him just what a serious commitment he had made. Though he never considered running away from what he saw as his responsibility, there were times when he deeply resented Robin for having disrupted what had been in his view a very uncomplicated and stable life.

'I never said this in so many words but I was very short and off-hand with Robin. I used to sigh a lot if we had to rearrange something because Robin wasn't up to going out and I made it quite clear that I didn't like having to change his sheets three times in the middle of the night because he was sweating so much. Robin usually put up with my moaning although I remember on one occasion he snapped back at me: "I didn't ask you to help you know." He was an incredibly thoughtful guy. It was him, for instance, who suggested we should get two single beds and exchange them for the double one that we'd shared up until then, and it was him who suggested I should also go to Lighthouse for counselling. But he never said it in such a way which sounded as if I needed it, but rather because it would give me a better understanding of what was going on with him.

'Overall Robin was a far more tolerant person than I am. For instance, he had been on nodding terms with his neighbour for several years and one day this neighbour suddenly started cutting him dead. I was convinced that this was because he'd found out Robin was gay and naturally suspected that he might have AIDS. It incensed me and I wanted to confront this man even though it didn't seem to bother Robin much. He said it was the man's prerogative not to acknowledge him if he didn't want to. But then one day Robin bumped into this man in the nearby off-licence and this time Robin made a point of going up to him and saying hello. To his surprise his neighbour greeted him like a long lost friend and was terribly apologetic. The straightforward explanation to his hitherto unfriendly behaviour was that he simply hadn't recognised Robin because he'd lost so much weight in the last few months.

'But I don't want to make Robin out to be a saint. It's natural to want to idolise the dead and I know Robin wouldn't have liked that. He had lots of faults. He was very fussy and very demanding in quite subtle ways and this got worse the iller he became.'

Steve had obviously been an excellent carer. He was lucky to have had friends who supported him and who would relieve him of his twenty-four-hour duty towards the end of Robin's life. His catering business suffered because for a year he had to hand the running of it over to a colleague who had neither the expertise nor the where-withall to make it profitable. It meant that money was very tight for a while and they lived off Robin's savings which he had kept in a building society for ten years waiting for a rainy day. 'It isn't going to rain any harder than this is it?' he once said to Steve who had questioned him on the wisdom of dipping into this reserve.

Steve himself admitted to me that: 'In the end I became a very good carer and a very good talker. In fact, at times I tried to get Robin to talk too much and didn't give him enough space. I was also extremely efficient at organising people to help and at making sure that Robin didn't get fed up with just seeing my face.

'We talked about his death because that was what he wanted and he always made it very easy for me. I remember the first time he said he wanted to start planning his funeral, I said something incredibly trite like, "Oh, come on, there's no need for that now," and under-standably he got quite cross with me and said, "For goodness sake, Steve, it's only a funeral and you'll be having one too one day." After that we had a laugh about it all. He had extremely catholic taste and his selection of music was very unconventional – ranging from Mahler to 'The Runaway Train'.

The fact that Robin knew he could have his funeral at Lighthouse made a huge difference to both him and Steve. Neither were particularly religious men and so a church or crematorium would have felt impersonal and unnatural. The Ian McKellen hall on the other hand was a place where Robin had often listened to music and taken part in relaxation classes. The building had become an important feature in his daily life and he planned it to be an important feature in his death.

When we talked once of Robin's death, Steve told me: 'I think he probably always had the upper hand in our relationship even when he was on the point of dying and ordered me to go out and buy some lemon sherbets. I had a feeling I shouldn't leave him but I did and when I came back I found that he'd gone into a coma and he never regained consciousness. I have the feeling that he wanted me out of the way when he died and if that's true then he got what he wanted because as far as I was concerned once he couldn't speak or move anymore he was as good as dead.'

For a long time after Robin's death, Steve became very depressed and withdrawn. Like so many carers of terminally ill people he suddenly found himself having to revert to his former lifestyle and a role which he had not occupied for many months. Till then every moment of the day had been dedicated to Robin and to Robin's care, and now there was nothing but a big blank to replace it. He continued to have counselling for many months after the death – attempting to come to terms with the loss of someone he had so deeply loved. It seemed to me that Steve had grown to love Robin more rather than less as the illness had progressed along its fatal course – probably because he found so much to admire in a man who, without denying the illness, truly managed to put it into a compartment whilst still getting on with other things that mattered to him. Even though this had sometimes been very difficult in practical terms, he somehow managed it by always keeping his mind active. He read and wrote incessantly – he wrote short stories, poems, letters to newspapers and even to his MP, as well as frequently using the phone in order to keep in touch with his friends, colleagues and family.

Although I met other couples at Lighthouse who were deeply committed to each other, the devotion that Steve and Robin had for each other was rare. They were unusual in their candid and occasionally droll attitude towards AIDS and in their ability to address whatever problem or crisis came upon them next. There was no doubt that both of them had been greatly changed by the experience of AIDS, and in many ways for the better, although after Robin's death Steve for some time seemed to manage much less well. He felt as if he was in a vacuum and could make no sense of his life which he saw as empty and meaningless.

Whenever he spoke to me about Robin he appeared animated but when he spoke about the present or his plans for the future he'd brush aside any attempt to confront his feelings. What happened in his counselling sessions I never knew because he was reluctant to talk in great detail about them but I could see they were an important part of his life and a vital safety net. I had no doubt that Steve would win through in the end. The grieving process has no set time span and for him it was likely to take a while longer yet. His continued association with Lighthouse as a place of memories might have been seen by some as an unhealthy attachment to the past but it was a coping strategy and a necessary step in breaking free from the old bonds.

· *Eight* ·

Nearly half the workers at London Lighthouse were volunteers – men and women of all ages who had chosen to give their services free of charge in order to help the centre function efficiently, and without whom the organisation would not have existed. Volunteers worked in every area of the building – in the kitchens, at the reception desk, on the residential unit, in fund raising and in day care. Also there were over 100 home support volunteers who worked in teams and who seldom came into the building because they visited and supported men and women with AIDS in their own homes throughout London.

On my induction course, one of the exercises involved looking at the word 'volunteer' and finding associations. Although most people put forward words such as 'good will', 'giving' and 'altruistic', some of us suggested words like 'unpaid', 'dog's body' and 'no status'. Contrary to this negative view, I had always liked the idea of being a volunteer but up till now the time had never been right or else the work had never sufficiently fired my enthusiasm.

What I learnt on the course was that volunteers at Lighthouse came from every avenue of society; they had to be clear about their own motivation; they had to be adaptable, they had to have a basic respect for people and a non-judgemental outlook. As long as people didn't bring with them any preconceived ideas or prejudice, knowledge about AIDS was not essential because it could be learned. Most importantly a volunteer had to find the right balance between meeting the needs of the organisation and his or her own needs.

Open meetings to recruit new volunteers were held bi-annually and during that process the organisers expected a natural selection to take place, in other words a certain proportion of people would drop out when they realised the commitment involved or the sort of work that would be expected of them. This was considered to be a very healthy process as it successfully eliminated most of those people who liked the idea of being a volunteer but who in reality would never have stood the course.

London Lighthouse expected from its volunteers commitment to working at certain tasks at certain times, an understanding of how crucial the issue of confidentiality was, the ability to communicate with paid members of staff, and a responsibility for setting and monitoring boundaries between a volunteer and a person being supported. In turn, a volunteer could expect help and support from paid members of staff, the possibility of shaping the policy and practice of the organisation, and the opportunity to experience what Lighthouse termed the 'gift relationship' between the volunteer and the person using the service. Like all social roles, the role of a volunteer had power implications and this 'gift relationship' was recognised as an intrinsically unequal one. The imbalance arose from the element of dominance often associated with power. To counter this attitude, people were encouraged to see power not as control over others but as the ability to achieve aims and objectives. Once volunteers acknowledged this, it would help redress the power imbalance. The empowerment of people with HIV was a central part of the philosophy of London Lighthouse and volunteers were expected both to assist in that empowerment and to experience it themselves.

Very occasionally, however, someone would get through the selection process, even though they were wholly unsuitable for the work and eventually they had to be asked to leave the organisation. I heard about one such woman who was said to have made racist remarks to the person she was supporting, who did nothing but spread gossip about the other members of her team and who pestered, to the point of adulation, a man with the virus. After having been cautioned several times, this woman was eventually asked to leave, but she put up strong resistance, accusing Lighthouse of underhand, oppressive behaviour and threatening to go to the press with her story. They were in fact empty threats and in the end she just disappeared and nothing more was heard of her.

The working relationship between staff and volunteers was usually a good one, though not always. I came across paid staff who were reluctant to ask a volunteer to do something either because they thought the volunteer was there out of good will and the job would bore them or because they thought the job was too 'important' to be done by someone who wasn't, in their view, trained to do it. One volunteer told me she was fed up with being given flowers for a job well done – but which any paid member of staff would be expected to do without reward.

The volunteers who did a lot of work (three or more shifts a week) tended to be older and often financially independent. This was not always the case, however. One man who worked on reception had taken early retirement from a fairly well-paid job where he had been running his own department and now survived by doing cleaning jobs so that he could devote the rest of his time to Lighthouse. Another volunteer was a milkman and although he wasn't entirely happy with his job, he kept it on as it enabled him to be at Lighthouse by 11.30 every morning.

Volunteers for home support training were especially carefully recruited. Whereas a volunteer in the centre could be supervised and any attitudes or behaviour contradicting London Lighthouse philosophy redirected, home support volunteers were left far more to their own devices. They would usually visit the person they were supporting on their own and any critical feedback would come only from the person being supported or from other members at the fortnightly team meetings.

The Home Support Service was provided by trained volunteers who were based in neighbourhood teams for mutual support. Each team met once a month to discuss the needs of all those being supported and as a means of providing a safe place to deal with the feelings that this work could bring up for volunteers.

But the nature of being a home support volunteer was changing. Originally it used to be more like the American style buddy one-to-one system, but by 1991 it had become apparent that sometimes the person with AIDS was less in need of support than that person's family or partner. Sheila, for instance, moved back home with her parents when she became too ill to fend for herself. She was a very self-sufficient person. Practising meditation gave her remarkable strength and a firm belief in the eternity of life, so that death did not seem to be a frightening prospect to her. Her parents on the other hand were terrified of AIDS and of losing their daughter. Although Sheila had known she was HIV positive as far back as 1986, she had not wanted her parents to know and had even tried to keep it from them when she finally developed KS in August 1990. Her parents brought her home from the hospital not yet realising the significance of her illness. But unable to face telling her parents the truth, Sheila had asked her sister to break the news to them and this was the first they learnt of their daughter's HIV status.

Her father was a mini-cab driver and her mother had recently retired from secretarial work due to ill health. Until Sheila became ill, AIDS for them was nothing more than a topic which provided journalists with juicy head-lines – as far removed from their own world as their thirty-two-year-old daughter's chaotic lifestyle had been. But they loved Sheila and willingly took her in when she became ill, prepared to do all they could to make her life and eventual death more comfortable.

The volunteer who supported her was called Rose. In the end she became the key link between Sheila and her parents. She visited their home in Ealing at least twice a week and would spend her time first talking to Sheila and then to her parents, she rarely saw all three together because that was the way they wanted it to be. Sheila's parents always had lots of questions to ask regarding her illness which they did not feel able to ask their daughter directly, although she would have liked them to. So Rose provided the role both of instructor and supporter. The questions she couldn't answer she found out from staff at Lighthouse and then would report back to Sheila's parents at the next visit.

Her relationship with all three was close though never intimate; this was because Sheila was an intensely private and self-sufficient person, and because her parents had set their own boundaries from their first meeting with Rose. Other than asking for information regarding the disease and a certain amount of practical and emotional support, they never asked any favour of her. This, however, did not prevent a great warmth growing up between Rose and Sheila's parents. She was the only person from London Lighthouse whom they allowed into their lives and the gratitude they felt towards her was considerable. For Rose it proved a very fruitful relationship because she was able to meet this couple's very specific needs. But she got to know their daughter less well because Sheila was proud of her independence and recognised that her parents needed as much if not more support than she did. Rose helped to make sure Sheila's parents – who looked after their daughter for two years – were able to continue in that role and offer their daughter the best possible care from home.

I don't think I would have liked to have been a home support volunteer and I'm pretty sure I wouldn't have made a very good one. It took a particular sort of person to give support to someone week in, week out, regardless of the demands made on them and of what was going on in their own personal life. I knew from talking to people that, while it could be a very rewarding experience, it could also be a punishing one, particularly if the person being supported was difficult or demented.

During the time I spent on the unit I met two people whom I subsequently visited at home and came to know well. There was one, though I saw him infrequently, whose company I enjoyed immensely. It was a relation-ship based on friendship and there was no need to establish boundaries. In the case of the other person, Kim, it was different. He was a man in his early thirties whom I first met while he was at Lighthouse for a week's respite care. I spent some time talking to him although even then I found him an aggressive and arrogant man. He was not particularly popular with the staff and nor were they particularly popular with him, but despite this mutual distrust he had frequently stayed on the unit. He was a self-confessed snob and complained a great deal about the food, the quality of care and the off-hand attitude of the nurses, and yet the unit was clearly a life-line for him and he later confided in me that he'd left a substantial amount of money to the organisation.

It didn't surprise me that during his week's stay he only had one visitor and she had come from the social services department to talk about his home-help situation. I was still fairly new to Lighthouse at the time, so when he asked me to come and see him the following week, I agreed because I felt rather sorry for this lonely man who clearly had no skills at making friends. I dare say I was also a little flattered at having been chosen out of so many staff and volunteers to visit him at home.

So, a week later I went to his house in Highgate – an hour's drive from where I lived – and spent the evening listening to stories about his life. It was the first of many visits which I'm afraid were soon to become a gruelling and unsatisfactory obligation, for what had begun out of pity continued out of duty and only came to an end with Kim's death in the summer of 1992. I would so like not to have felt this way but the truth was that I did and it was better to face this fact than to pretend that the visits were in some way pleasurable.

The basic problem was that, after three months of knowing Kim and having visited him all of half a dozen times, I had to admit to myself that I did not much care for the man. This was because he was not a particularly likeable person and the absence of any support network in his life was testimony to this fact. He had no friends or relatives to speak of, only two or three other people who, like me, visited him on a regular basis. I never did find out what they thought of Kim but I suspect it was not easy for them either.

Not having known Kim before he became ill, it was hard to know how much of his capricious nature was HIV related and how much was an already well-established personality trait. I would imagine that he had never been a particularly sympathetic person but that his illness exacerbated the negative aspects of his character making him generally more angry, more needy and more disinhibited. We only ever spoke about what was happening in his life and he rarely asked me anything about myself, but I did not mind since I knew he had very few people to talk to and the very least I could do was provide a receptacle for his outbursts. But the conversation often became repetitive and vindictive with him criticising people who had annoyed or offended him.

On several occasions he told me his life story. His father had worked for the Armed Forces and he'd spent most of his childhood abroad. Having become aware of his sexuality at the age of ten during a camping holiday in the South of France, he became lonely and introspective. From then on, he said, he felt like an outsider because he knew he was different from the other boys in his class. It had been particularly difficult living among small-minded army folk where everyone had been expected to conform, so at the age of seventeen he left home and came to London where he managed to earn just enough to live off by doing several part-time jobs including at one time working as a rent boy. Later, by contrast, he made a great deal of money when he started his own management consultancy business. He had never had a boyfriend and professed to never having wanted close friendships. If you had no expectations then you were never disappointed, he argued.

He admitted that he had only ever had two interests in life – sex and ballet – and he was extremely knowledgeable on both subjects, but part of his present crisis was that he now felt too ill to take an interest in either. On one occasion he confided in me that he had no libido left and this made him feel as if his life had already ended. He was coping badly with the disease and sometimes I found it extremely hard to offer any words of comfort – not because I did not feel like it but because words of sympathy so often express hopeful sentiments such as, 'I'm sure you'll feel better soon.' But I came to realise that where AIDS was concerned such false reassurance was wholly inappropriate and could even be interpreted as deceitful. Just listening and showing concern for his pain and anxiety seemed to do little good and I felt very ineffectual because I was incapable of improving the quality of his life. Nothing would lift his spirits and as each new infection took a hold of him, he became more and more depressed. He was sick of being sick and incensed with the injustice of it all. As an occasional church goer, he railed against God for allowing such a tragedy to happen to him, as opposed to those he felt were more deserving of divine retribution.

When I first met Kim he had been HIV positive for two years. He'd had several minor complaints all of which caused him discomfort as opposed to actual pain. His skin, for instance, was very rough and he had several sore patches round his mouth and on his arms. His appetite was poor and he had swollen glands in his neck and armpits. He had difficulty swallowing and persistent periods of nausea and dizziness. He never suffered from all these symptoms simultaneously, but usually at least two or three of them would afflict him at any one time.

Six months after I met him, he started having fits and

was rushed to hospital with toxoplasmosis – an abscess in the brain. This was diagnosed through a brain scan and successfully treated with a course of injections. Later he succumbed to candida in the gullet and then finally to cytomegalovirus (CMV) which seriously impaired his vision for the last few weeks of his life. He lost a further stone in weight and finally did not have the strength, or indeed the will, to fight on. During the last few months of his life he admitted to wishing the end would come quickly because he was terrified of a slow, painful death. I noticed that he had got to the point of being so afraid of his illness that he was almost afraid of himself. I think he probably always possessed a fair degree of self-loathing, although his pride would never have allowed him to acknowledge that fact.

Thinking about him now, I wish that I could find some redeeming qualities to write about Kim but I cannot, except perhaps that I felt he had every excuse in the world to be as difficult as he liked. I never tried to admonish him for criticising just about everyone he came in contact with because there seemed little point – once he had made up his mind about someone nothing would change it.

He was a wealthy man but only rarely displayed any sign of generosity. The one occasion I can think of was when he offered to buy me a car so that I could take him on trips to the country. My own car was so clapped out and unreliable that he knew a new car was the only way I'd agree to taking him out. He was very keen for me to become more involved in his life and got easily annoyed when I couldn't or wouldn't do as he wished. He tried to persuade me to accept his offer of a car by saying it would make his life worth living again. I felt appalled and compromised by this emotional blackmail. While having no intention of accepting his offer, I admonished myself for not being a more caring and selfless person. Why, for instance, didn't I get my own car fixed and give up a few of my precious Saturdays to take Kim down to Brighton or Southend? And yet I knew it wouldn't have actually made him any happier and I also knew that, as a volunteer, it was no good doing things out of obligation and in the end resenting them. In the event my excuses were unnecessary as shortly after this Kim became too sick even to travel up the road, let alone out of London.

One member of staff got quite cross with me once when I told him about my feelings towards Kim. 'You shouldn't go,' he said, 'it's no good for either of you if you go out of pity.' But despite this advice I continued to go right up until the end. I did not want to let him down and although I always dreaded making that journey across London, it was never actually quite as bad as I'd anticipated. I should have liked to have gone a little less than once every two weeks but he always rang to fix the next appointment a week after my last visit and I generally conceded to his demands.

With hindsight, I realised that the whole problem with my relationship with Kim was that I never established any boundaries. Very early on I should have made it clear to him that I couldn't visit him more than once a month and that on those occasions I couldn't stay for more than three hours. I should have challenged him if I disagreed with the slanderous things he said about other people and I should have expressed my displeasure when his demands became too persistent. But instead I suppressed my indignity and in the end compromised and gave in. Because I knew Kim was terminally ill, I didn't want to rock the boat.

Part of the problem was that I had got myself into a home support situation without having adequate back-up and support. No one knew I was visiting Kim and, had I been a home support volunteer, I would have had a key worker at Lighthouse and other volunteers with whom to talk through these difficulties on a regular basis. When I found myself pregnant at the beginning of 1992 I did ease off the visits and though he didn't understand how anyone could possibly feel tired and ill when expecting a baby, he had no choice but to accept my excuses.

It would have been a lie to say that I did not feel a hint of relief at Kim's death – not only because I did not have to make those long and difficult visits anymore but also because the release that he had so been waiting for had finally come. But when the news was broken to me on the phone I was surprised to find my eyes filling with tears. I had not been intimate with or close to Kim in any way but on hearing of his death I discovered that somewhere, buried deep inside, lingered a reluctant fondness for the man.

I do not look back on my relationship with him with any sense of pride or achievement. Although I know I gave him as much as I could give him at the time, I did not manage to overcome my own negative feelings towards him, nor did I change my begrudging attitude towards my visits. I did, however, manage to respect him – for although he could never be described as someone who had lived and died well with AIDS, he managed to take care of himself and remained alone in his flat until two weeks before he died despite receiving very little practical or emotional support. Although he had failed to furnish his life with meaningful relationships – which meant that there was no one with him when he died – I think in his own way he did feel a degree of warmth for the two or three volunteers with whom he worked hard to keep in contact and whom in the end I believe he came to trust. I am only sorry I never felt more warmth towards him myself and that I was not able to make his life a little more tolerable.

Kim's funeral took me by surprise as he had never discussed the arrangements with me. I knew only that he had employed a solicitor at great cost, because he thought those available free of charge from various AIDS charities were no good. It was held in a large Anglican church in North London because he had occasionally worshipped there during his years of living in London. There was a choir and a string quartet, and the coffin was a hand-carved solid American oak casket with ornate brass fittings. At the end of the service everyone was handed a red rose.

About twenty people attended and although I felt it was an excellent turnout, we were nonetheless completely dwarfed by the size and grandeur of the church. Afterwards everyone went back to Kim's flat where a catering firm had prepared a lavish buffet lunch. This unexpected display of generosity accompanied by such a spectacular exit from life seemed wholly uncharacteristic and I found something both endearing and disconcerting in it all. Kim had obviously spent a lot of time and a great deal of money planning his funeral and I got the feeling that it had probably given him more pleasure than anything else in his life at that time. The way in which he had kept it a secret from all of us was his way of making a final dramatic statement with his death in a way that he had never succeeded in doing with his life.

· Nine ·

When I'd only been at Lighthouse a few days a volunteer of long-standing warned me that I would find my time on the residential unit both taxing and draining. 'It's a very, very stressful place to be,' he added, 'and you'll have to find your own way.' He finished off by telling me that the work up there didn't suit everybody. I had indeed already met volunteers who preferred to work on the ground floor where there was more structure and continuity to their day. There were also a few who didn't want to work on the unit because of being too close to very sick people – these were often volunteers who themselves had the virus and who wished to keep the physical rigours of the disease at arm's length.

There were also those who went to work on the residential unit but didn't like it when they got there due to the unstructured nature of the work which made them feel uncomfortable and without any defined role. I had also heard of one or two who were just plain lazy and only wanted to sit with residents and hold hands with the dying. When they were told that other more menial tasks were also expected of a volunteer, they would leave in a huff. One volunteer who'd worked on the unit longer than anybody said to me: 'I think some of them just come out of a sense of curiosity because they want to see what a person with AIDS looks like.'

My first days on the unit were spent working in the kitchen assisting the chef who made the residents their breakfasts in a small kitchen at the end of the corridor, and organising their lunches and dinners to be brought up from the main kitchen on the ground floor. This was where I learnt all about hygiene – not for my own benefit but for the protection of the residents. There were naturally a great many bugs flying about the place and while a particular infection might be harmless to one person, for another it could be fatal.

I was shown round by Sister Peter, one of the two volunteers (both nuns) who took it in turns to collect the residents' menu orders and hand out the meals. It was a long and painstaking procedure, particularly when it involved persuading people who didn't feel hungry to choose food that they may want to eat in several hours time. Sister Peter had worked on the unit for a year. She had started out as a volunteer in the main kitchen but then her very considerable listening skills had been noticed and she'd been asked if she would prefer to work on the residential unit. She told me she loved it there because she could be nearer the residents who were 'such lovely, lovely people'.

She was magnificent in her patience and quiet understanding. Nothing riled her and although drug abuse and the gay scene couldn't have been further from her experience, she possessed a genuine acceptance and respect of other people's lifestyles. She would embrace anyone who came within two feet of her, and later when I was myself to go through a very painful time at Lighthouse, she held my hand so tightly that I felt an energy in her grasp. She would sit for hours at people's bedsides when they were dying and, if asked to do so, would talk about God and of the better times that lay ahead.

The meals were quite a muddle with everyone wanting different things at different times. They had to be brought up in the lift from the kitchens and then reheated in the microwave at the resident's request (this later changed due to new hygiene regulations). Some of the residents were very thin and looked at the menu over and over again trying desperately to find something that wouldn't make them feel even more nauseous.

Everyone liked to talk about the food at Lighthouse, and opinions varied enormously. There were those who thought it excellent and those who found it dull and disappointing. The most common complaint I heard was that it was not as good as it had previously been. As far as I could see the standard seemed to vary enormously. There were days when everyone was satisfied and days when no one was satisfied. The cafe had been losing money since it opened so measures such as giving smaller portions or using up everything in store before purchasing anything new had been adopted and predictably weren't at all popular. At one time chicken appeared on the menu five days running which provoked comments in the Suggestions Book such as: 'Is the head of catering married to Bernard Matthews?'

One of the nurses was surprised that Lighthouse didn't have a dietician since the holistic approach which it proposed made a strong connection between diet and a person's general well-being. But one man's meat is another man's poison – some complained the food was too exotic and spicy for people with delicate stomachs while others said that it was too bland and not appealing enough to attract the public in from outside. Once or twice I heard people praise the food unreservedly. Bob –

once an actor – who had been on the unit for four weeks when I arrived, and died a month later, had come from Westminster Hospital where he said the food had been 'unparalleled in its awfulness'. Consequently he would enthuse with passion about Lighthouse food.

Going round with the menus meant that I was able very quickly to get to know the residents. There were at least three who were in for terminal care and, as they grew weaker, it became a quite pointless exercise trying to persuade them to eat anything other than ice cream or mashed banana. One of the residents who was in for palliative care and who had been on the unit for seven weeks asked me to feed him a bowl of custard which I agreed to willingly although I had a feeling he was capable of doing it himself. He asked me three times if I minded and each time I told him that I didn't which was true although I suppose in all honesty I didn't particularly like it either. It seemed strange that it could feel so natural to feed a small child and so unnatural to feed a grown man.

Of the other residents, several were quite seriously ill suffering from one or more of the opportunistic infections which affect people with HIV and the rest had not much outwardly wrong with them except that they or their partners needed a rest.

The tasks of a volunteer on the residential unit were many and varied, from sorting out the linen cupboard to holding the hand of a dying resident. Sometimes it could be very demanding and exhausting work and at other times it could be highly enjoyable and even entertaining, such as the day when two residents asked me to come down to the Ian McKellen hall to hear them rehearse a piece for a London Lighthouse benefit concert to be held some time during the following month. Both were professional musicians and while one played the organ, the other sang – mostly songs from musicals which I did not recognise. They were extremely talented and entertaining but I couldn't help feeling a little guilty at having left the unit for so long. On returning I apologised to the charge nurse who seemed completely unbothered by my absence and told me that being in the Ian McKellen hall listening to music once in a while was just as important as being at the nurse's station and answering the telephone.

There were also occasions when I had to accompany residents to a hospital appointment. My first hospital visit was with Lucca, an Italian man who had once owned a restaurant in Soho. We spent the best part of the day together in Westminster Hospital and afterwards in a taxi driving to various destinations where he had business to attend to. What I had been told would take two hours in the end took six.

In Westminster Hospital Lucca first had a dental appointment, then we went up to the AIDS ward to see his doctor, then to the radiology department to have an X-ray and finally to the prescriptions counter to collect some drugs. Compared to Lighthouse I found Westminster Hospital a drab and impersonal place possessing that metalic, cabbagey smell which pervades the corridors of most NHS hospitals. The care for AIDS patients was considered excellent there but I felt the stifling atmosphere could hardly be conducive to good health. Lucca spoke warmly of Lighthouse, particularly since he had previously only heard negative things about it – namely that you had to be rich to go there, that the food was lousy and the nurses lazy. In his experience none of this was true and he had been especially touched by the way staff in the cafe had thought to make him a sandwich before he left because they realised he would not be back in time for lunch.

Few volunteers worked the night shift from 10 p.m. to 7 a.m. I only did it five times because I found it too tiring and disruptive to my routine. On the last of these occasions there was a call from reception at 11.30 saying that Joe was on the line. The call was then put through and there was silence the other end. 'Hello Joe,' I said, at which the voice on the other end erupted in anger, shouting: 'How did you know my name? I haven't given my name to anyone.' As it happened this was true but most staff were sufficiently familiar with his calls to recognise his voice. I explained this to him and although he didn't seem in the least bit reassured, he went ahead and told me why he was calling. He wanted to speak to a woman who worked in community services and I told him she had undoubtedly left the building several hours ago. He wouldn't accept this however and insisted I call her at home to give her a message. I told him that I didn't have her home number and suggested that he spoke to a nurse instead. At this he hung up.

Two hours later a call came through from St Mary's Hospital to say that he had been brought in having taken an overdose. I felt terrible about it. I knew I couldn't have prevented it but I still felt in some way responsible. I was reassured, however, by one of the nurses when she told me that this sort of thing happened frequently with Joe. He had been mentally ill for many years, long before he became infected with HIV. The nurses recognised that a place like London Lighthouse could do very little to help someone like Joe.

There was a fast turnover rate on the residential unit. Three weeks was usually the maximum time that people stayed, though cases were frequently reviewed and when someone was terminally ill the question of a departure date didn't arise. It was possible to work out who was terminally ill because 'P' for palliative care was written by their name on the board in the nurse's office. There were twenty-four beds in all and often there was a dilemma about where to put whom. For instance, when I first arrived on the unit there was a frantic juggling of beds going on since three of the six rooms were occupied by women and the remaining three occupied by residents who were terminally ill. The problem was that someone was due to come in who was known to be problematic and who had recently made several suicidal gestures. The question was who would be most able to tolerate having him in the bed next to them.

Several weeks later, however, the atmosphere on the unit changed. No one was terminally ill, only two residents wanted their meals brought up to them on a tray and there were parties in the TV room every evening. Then a few weeks after that the atmosphere changed once again. Although the nurses were unusually quiet because most residents were self-medicating and none required any complicated treatment, a lot of people on the unit were suffering from psychological problems and the nurses, all of whom had some training in counselling skills, were finding their energies taken up in other directions. The counselling department and Father John White, who provided pastoral care, were often called up to the unit to help residents when anxiety, mood disturbances and mild or severe depression took a grip.

The mood of the unit changed as residents and rotas changed. When I started working many nurses and domestics (or residential unit assistants as they later became known) commented on the fact that recently things had been particularly hard on the unit. Two residents who had stayed on a number of occasions since Lighthouse opened and whom everyone had grown extremely fond of had died in quick succession of each other.

I saw many people come and go and, although some only stayed for a short while, I remember with remarkable clarity the people I met during my first few weeks on the residential unit. I'm not sure why this should be because I certainly didn't get to know all of them but as I had dicovered whenever travelling in a foreign country everything was particularly vivid and my powers of observation were considerably sharpened. In the space of just a few days the people I met who had AIDS taught me more than the countless textbooks I had read.

There was a young man called Arthur with progressive multifocal lucoencepolopathy (PML). This is one of the nastiest of the neurological diseases. The papova virus lives in the brain and when someone's immune system ceases to function it starts to activate and holes appear in the brain cells. Only about 5 per cent of people with HIV get PML but there is no treatment and the time between diagnosis and death is usually not longer than eighteen weeks. Six months before I met him Arthur had been an AIDS counsellor and had initiated several school education programmes. Now, all round the unit were signs with his name on and arrows pointing in the direction of his room in case he wandered off unsupervised. On the wall above his bed was a handwritten notice telling him what day of the week it was and the name of the nurse who was on duty that day.

Then there was Rachel who was suffering from toxoplasmosis. Toxoplasmosis of the central nervous system is one of the most common of the life-threatening opportunistic infections which people with AIDS get. It is a brain disorder which is caused by the reactivation of a previous infection. Studies have shown that nearly a third of AIDS patients who have been exposed to toxoplasma gordie (the parasite which causes the infection) will develop the disease within two years of their AIDS diagnosis. She was suffering from chronic limb weakness and having periodic fits. There were also two young men in their early twenties, George and Paul, both currently undergoing a gruelling programme of chemotherapy for lymphomas at Westminster Hospital, a cancer which effects the white blood cells in the glands. The outlook for both was poor.

George had arrived on the unit the same morning I started work there and by the end of the day he had received a stream of visitors – all young, handsome, athletic-looking men. He was obviously extremely popular and pinned up his numerous get-well cards all over the walls. His coordination was poor and he walked on crutches; one eye was droopy and half closed, he had KS all over his face, and he complained of his temperature fluctuating so much that at one moment he needed ice packs to cool him down and at the next hot water bottles to keep him warm.

One of his room-mates complained to a nurse about the number of visitors he was receiving, as well as the mess George had made by leaving his clothes littered all over the floor. There was nothing the nurses could do to prevent this since the whole ethos of Lighthouse said that the unit belonged to the residents and as such they could – within reason – treat it like their own home. As long as they were well enough it was up to them whether they kept their space tidy or not.

A few days later I accompanied George to buy some cigarettes and since he walked very slowly we managed to have quite a talk. He was a very open person who appeared to be coping well with his illness despite having much wrong with him. When I told him I admired his frankness, he said he didn't know how much he was repressing. I suggested that maybe his approach to the disease was more straightforward and open-minded than most people's and therefore there was less to repress in the first place, but he just laughed saying, 'My friends call me devious.'

His KS showed up as purple blotches on his face and he was looking forward to having some camouflage lessons from Sheila Dutch who was specially trained in the technique. He said he only intended to use it on certain occasions, for instance when he went to a gay club because when he was there he could see the level of fear rising as soon as he entered the room. Elsewhere he was determined not to use make-up because, as he said, 'This is where I am at the moment with this disease and if other people can't cope with it then that's their problem.'

His main concern seemed to be that the friend he rented a room from shouldn't be burdened with the responsibility of having to look after him once he'd left Lighthouse and he was keen to find a council flat before too long. The other thing that worried him was that his ex-partner, who was younger than him, might be HIV positive. He said he couldn't bear living with the knowledge that he had infected a person he still loved dearly. It then emerged that this man had in fact tested negative, but that George had not been reassured by the news since he had heard of several people testing negative despite being positive all along.

Children were becoming an increasingly common sight on the residential unit, since more and more women were using the services at Lighthouse. Teresa was one of the first women I met on the unit. She was from Kenya and had come for a three week stay although sadly she

deteriorated suddenly while at Lighthouse and died unexpectedly after only seventeen days. Her five-year-old son
was almost always with her and since his mother was
hardly able to entertain him, he had learnt the skills of
self-amusement. For such a young child, he was amaz-
ingly resourceful and surprisingly unperturbed by his
mother's failing health. He seemed happy to draw or read
most of the day and seldom got in the way of the nurses.

Teresa would smile a lot but there was never any joy in
her smile, just a resigned acceptance of the way things
were. She didn't communicate easily and seemed oblivi-
ous to what was going on around her. One day when she
was sitting in the day room smoking a cigarette, I asked
her whether she had any more children. At first she didn't
answer but later she told me that she had three other
children who were all at home with her husband and
whom she didn't want to be bothered with anymore.

I wondered what exactly she meant by this. There was
no doubt that she loved all four of her children but at this
particular time she didn't want any of them around her,
not even the youngest who was only there because there
was no one else to look after him. Was it a form of self-
protection to make leaving them that much easier? Teresa
was now so poorly and so demoralised by the physical
changes taking place in her body that she was unable to
see anything beyond her illness, and this left no room for
anyone else in her life, not even her own children. In other
words, she had already given up the struggle and wanted
now to be left alone to die in peace. Her children were
disturbing that process by constantly trying to drag her
back into life; because in the normal scheme of things
Teresa should have been there to raise them into
adulthood.

Watching how AIDS decimated whole families was the

thing I found most distressing about the time I spent working at Lighthouse. I once sat in a meeting next to a man from Zimbabwe who was HIV positive and whose wife and two children were also positive. I could, possibly, imagine coming to terms with my own death from AIDS, but how on earth did you also come to terms with the knowledge that your child, or children, had been infected with the virus, which had been passed on to them *in utero*? What these parents had to endure was a torture quite incomprehensible to me.

There were few such families using Lighthouse services although the numbers were increasing with more and more families coming forward in need of home support. In the Community Services Department it demanded an entirely new area of training in home care which had previously not been required. Sometimes whole families had the virus, sometimes only a few members. The random nature of this selection process was cruel in the extreme with 20 to 25 per cent of children born to women with HIV carrying the virus.

Beatrice was the woman I came to know best at Lighthouse. I had first met her at reception when she had locked her keys in the car with the engine running and so I was pleased to see a familiar face during my first week on the residential unit. She had a child of seven years old who was born three years before she became infected. I met her at a time of immense sorrow in her life as she had recently made the decision to send her daughter back to Ireland to live with her ex-husband who was now remarried with two more small children of his own. It was a terrible decision to have to make but Beatrice thought it best for Chloe and probably best for herself too in the end. She was nonetheless devastated by the thought of losing the person she cherished most in the whole world.

Having a young daughter of my own, I greatly sympathised with her anguish, although knowing that I was unlikely ever to experience such a terrible loss myself, I couldn't completely fathom its depths. How Beatrice coped, managing in the midst of all this to have a good time and keep her sense of humour, staggered me and yet in her ashen face and sunken eyes there was a look of such sorrow as to tell a story of monumental pain.

Beatrice was very popular with the nurses on the unit. When she arrived for her fourth visit she was exhausted and very weak and I noticed that those nurses who knew her best seemed distressed at how much worse she had become since her last visit. Beatrice, however, was unaware of their concern and was determined to use her two-week stay effectively. Her goal was to build up her strength and put on a stone in weight. She felt she had every chance of doing this as one of the nurses told me that, on her first visit eighteen months ago, she had weighed just six stone and had been confined to a wheelchair.

Her life was very complicated. She had been living with a man for the past three and a half years. Apparently he had had two HIV tests, both of which had proved negative, but I wasn't sure how conscientious they were in their attitude towards safer sex as two months previously she had discovered she was pregnant. After a moment's deliberation she had decided to have the pregnancy terminated because of the risks of passing the virus on to the child. Also, she knew she no longer had the strength to look after a baby. Her partner, she felt, would have been able to cope had the baby been well, but in the event of it having positive antibodies she felt he would probably have abandoned them both.

She stressed to me so often that she was in a stable and

loving relationship, that I couldn't help doubting her, particularly since during the whole of her time on the unit, her boyfriend only visited her once. Beatrice occupied one of the single rooms, the wall of which she had covered with pictures of her daughter. She wrote to Chloe everyday, talked about her incessantly and rang her frequently. What made the separation just about manageable was that Chloe was obviously extremely happy with her Irish relatives, although unaware that the move would probably prove to be permanent.

Although Beatrice was suffering from a degree of HIV-related dementia, to someone like myself who had not known her before, there were few visible signs. She seemed a bit scatter-brained and at times eccentric but I suspected she had always been a little that way. She still had remarkable powers of concentration and would read for hours curled up in her bed with classical music simultaneously blaring from an old and decrepit-looking portable radio.

Beatrice was in her late thirties. She had been a drug user for most of her twenties but with the help of a close friend, and motivated by regular attendance at NA meetings, she had stopped using drugs shortly before the birth of her daughter. She said she hadn't taken anything since 1985 and was indeed so determined to stay clean that she refused to take any medication containing opiates. She had also been teetotal for three years and her latest triumph was giving up smoking. Believing that the toxins in cigarettes put an additional strain on the immune system, she wanted to give her body the best possible chance to stay healthy.

She told me that although her HIV status terrified her at times, it had also proved to be a great motivator as her diagnosis had come at a critical moment in her life, when she had been flirting with the idea of using drugs again. Her diagnosis, she said, had the effect of prompting her to take control once again and kick the habit for good. I suggested that it might equally have gone the other way and prompted her to abuse further, but she assured me that she was the sort of person who liked a challenge and didn't give up easily. 'Once I'd realised that a drug habit, on top of HIV, would only serve to shorten my life, I knew I had to ditch it once and for all,' she said.

When Beatrice left the unit she was very much better. With so much sickness about it was very easy to forget that many people came in looking and feeling wretched but left a week or two later greatly improved. It never ceased to amaze me how people like Beatrice rallied and managed repeatedly to make remarkable come-backs. She left the unit feeling optimistic, planning a holiday and having decided to start an aromatherapy course with the idea of going into practice some day. Before she left she held a small party for the nurses, volunteers and other residents on the unit because she loved Lighthouse and was always sorry to leave. She told me that from the first day she came here her attitude towards her illness changed. At the time she had only recently been diagnosed as having HIV and, with only the media-constructed image of a skeleton in her mind, she felt altogether 'powerless, pathetic and doomed'. But at Lighthouse, she said, everyone seemed to be 'positive and glowing'. Although they had the virus they were getting out, starting new relationships and training for new careers. The message was that life went on.

On rare occasions Lighthouse was unable to help an individual, as in the case of Aphra, a woman in her late thirties from Zambia. She had only recently been diag- nosed with HIV and had minor complaints of candida and thrush but the knowledge that she had been infected had knocked her off balance and thrown her into a state of shock. For the first few days on the unit she sat in her single room staring at the wall; if she wasn't staring at the wall she was asleep. Her family would phone frequently but I couldn't persuade her to speak to them. She just shook her head and sank back against the wall. When she spoke it was only to refuse a cup of tea or a slice of toast, and she seemed to drag the words to the surface so that every single syllable felt like a colossal effort.

Aphra, it transpired, had acute reactive depression, which amounted to a total denial of the diagnosis. A counsellor went to see her but decided that she needed clinical treatment. 'At the moment she's in a state where she seems to have no emotions, so talking about them would be fruitless,' he said. From further investigation it was discovered that Aphra had a history of mental illness and so a few days later was transferred to an acute psychiatric ward. She remained on the unit for ten days in all and her presence, though silent and undemanding, affected everyone who tried to coax her out of a state of mind which was impenetrable and repressive.

Cases like Aphra were very rare, although practically all people diagnosed with HIV needed some sort of counselling or psychological input in helping them cope with the illness. AIDS was all about loss – the loss of one's health, one's freedom, one's future and very often the loss of relationships, family and work as well. For some people all of these things happened simultaneously, in which case the effect could be devastating. It could literally mean that one day everything was normal and the next day your future and your security had been snatched from underneath you.

Jamie – a gay man in his mid-thirties – described his

sense of loss to me like this: 'I felt I had died inside but my body lived on. Everything in my life had been snatched from me. I was walking around seeing the same things about me but it was different eyes looking at them. I was talking to the same people in the street but it was a different voice uttering those words. So almost the worst thing about it was the sense that I had lost myself.'

I met Jamie in my third week of working on the unit. I liked him the best of everybody I met on the unit because we had a lot in common and I felt he was a kindred spirit. I didn't find friendships were always spontaneous at Lighthouse but Jamie was different and almost immediately we began to chat about things other than AIDS. He was one of the first residents I met who seemed genuinely interested in my life. He brought me slides of some of his early sculptures and I brought him pictures of my daughter.

Jamie had lost everything. He'd been living and working in Australia for over ten years when he was diagnosed with ARC (Aids Related Complex). He had not had an excessive number of partners and had been practising safe sex for five years, hoping to escape the fate of so many of his peer group. But when the effects of HIV infection became prevalent he returned to England where he knew he could get free medical care.

When Jamie returned to England he was compelled to stay with his parents in Leeds for the first few months since he had nowhere else to go. This was probably the worst time: 'First I told them that I was gay and then I told them that I had AIDS. My mother had always had an inkling but had never been able to accept my sexuality, which she saw as abnormal, so I wanted to spell it out to her. I think it was harder for her to hear that I was gay than to hear that I had a terminal illness. Of course, she created a scene and went around the place making a scene, completely unable to offer me any kind of comfort. My father, by contrast, just withdrew as he always does. I wanted to create a scene too. I wanted to say to my mother, "You're responsible for me, you're responsible for the way I've turned out, and so you're responsible for the fact that I've got AIDS." Thankfully I never did say these things because it isn't true and it wouldn't have been fair but it shows what an unsatisfactory relationship we have.

'They couldn't bear the shame and although I wouldn't have minded them telling other family members and close friends they insisted that it should remain a secret. So when I bumped into an old family friend in the street who said, "I'm so sorry to hear you've got cancer," I was incensed and I told her outright that I didn't have cancer and I didn't know where she'd got that information from. Not surprisingly the poor woman was terribly embarrassed.

'I guess my parents weren't entirely surprised that I was gay but the two things coming together acted as a mortal blow and I think severed our relationship for good. We've never been close and this meant the wedge between us has been driven even deeper. In the end I couldn't stand it any longer and I came up to London.'

Jamie said that when he heard parents talking to their children at Lighthouse it filled him with regret because although these parents may not have understood everything and may have felt acutely uncomfortable in such an unfamiliar environment, at least they were struggling to come to terms with their child's diagnosis and to understand the problems.

When I met Jamie he was on the point of being housed

by Camden council, having slept for three months on an ex-lover's floor. He'd left all his close friends in Australia and was having to create a new life for himself in whatever time was left to him. I always looked forward to seeing him and when I worked nights I would sit on the end of his bed and pass the time away chatting since he suffered from insomnia. I liked his sense of irony and the way he looked at the world. He described himself as homophobic because he felt uneasy in the company of gay men. 'As a child I became so adept at putting on masks, that I forgot to take them off again,' he told me once.

I kept on seeing Jamie long after he left Lighthouse and watched him steadily decline and then claw his way back into a state of remission. He wasn't ready for death, he told me, because he hadn't yet discovered how to make an adventure out of it. He suffered from pneumothorax several times. He told me how he'd been in hospital once when a terrible pain had racked his body for hours. Doctors had come to assess his condition and nurses had set up and adjusted apparatus but unlike in the Lighthouse he felt no one had bothered to tell him what was going on or to offer him any words of comfort. 'I felt powerless and desperate and more alone than I've ever felt in my entire life because at the end of the day I knew there was just me alone in my body. I felt as if I were dangling on a string and that somehow I had to keep a hold of that string because it was my only hope of survival. It would have been so easy to let go.'

What I admired most about Jamie was that he didn't possess an ounce of self-pity. That's not to say he didn't get angry and irritable and he told me once that he couldn't begin to understand people who said they were living well with AIDS. 'I hate, detest and resent every bit of this disease,' he said. If there was anything productive in it for him, it was simply that he had had to take a good hard look at himself. 'When you're sitting in the same room day after day you begin to get cabin fever and your mind starts working in a totally different way. People come and go, leaving me with snippets of information about their lives and about the world outside and then they leave and go back to their homes and their busy lives while I'm left alone to chew over what's been said. I have to home in on all the tiny details because there's no broader picture anymore.'

I saw myself in that picture. My life was becoming impossibly busy. At times I felt I was standing on the edge of chaos trying to do everything thoroughly and efficiently and yet knowing I couldn't. I felt I was missing out on seeing my daughter grow from a baby into a toddler, leaving my husband too often to cope with rebuilding our recently bought ramshackle of a house. At the same time my role as a volunteer at Lighthouse was proving far more of a commitment than I'd at first intended. I should have liked to see Jamie much more often but he was so considerate of my other ties and obligations that I felt absolved and sadly saw him infrequently.

As he grew iller, I saw the difference in our lives magnified, forming an inevitable separation. That was not to say that I didn't feel as close and tender towards him as I had always done but we had never had time to explore or share things as equals. I met him when he was relatively well and independent and in a matter of months he had become housebound and extremely sick. His illness was now his life, his sole topic of conversation, and I had become one of those visitors who walked in and walked out leaving snippets of information behind me for him to ponder and pick over.

Jamie had mixed feelings about London Lighthouse. Though he had greatly appreciated the care and attention given to him by the nurses and volunteers, he found it an unrelaxing place to be in. As someone who liked to sleep alone and who was disturbed by the slightest noise at night, sharing a room with two other restless men was far from ideal. He also found the sight and sound of chronic illness distressing because he saw it as a signal of what lay ahead.

For two weeks he shared a room with Bob, although they never exchanged more than a few words. Bob liked to maintain a certain degree of privacy and was apt to hide himself away behind the curtains and cut himself off into one corner of the room. It was his way of telling people not to get close and Jamie respected this. Although he would have liked to get to know Bob better, he sensed that the curtains represented an iron-tight barrier. 'I suppose he knew he didn't have much time left and felt it was pointless trying to make new friends,' Jamie observed.

Nevertheless he was riveted by Bob's conversations and couldn't help eavesdropping when he talked to his mother on the telephone or to the numerous friends who dropped in with tasty homemade pies and pâtés. In the three weeks that Jamie was at Lighthouse Bob's disembodied voice became something of a guide for him. As he listened day after day to Bob's opinions and predictions, he grew to admire a man who was clearly in control of the way he wished to live the last stages of his life. Several weeks after Jamie had left Lighthouse we were talking on the phone when he asked me how 'la Bob' was, hoping to hear tales of further eccentricities. 'Oh, didn't you know,' I said, rather too matter-of-factly, 'he died last week.' I did not know then the effect Bob had had on Jamie and had I done so I would certainly have tried to soften the blow a little. However Jamie said later that, although the news shocked him at first and he thought to himself 'typical journalist to tell me in such a blunt manner', later he realised that this was exactly the right way to have found out. Bob's death was no big deal because Bob wouldn't have considered it as a big deal.

Ever since I started working on the unit I was fascinated by this intriguing figure who hid behind his screens, demanding his meals punctually at the same time every day, insisting on taking a two-hour bath every second morning, and getting easily irritated when people did things not exactly to his liking. One or two people found him an extreme bore, but generally he was respected and admired. I had been on the reception desk when he first arrived at Lighthouse and at the time had been shocked by his extremely emaciated body. His appearance continued to shock me every time I saw him. When I got talking to him later, he said, 'I've always been much too thin, dear, so I had an unfair advantage from the beginning.'

Getting to talk to him took three weeks of persistence on my part. Every time I looked in to see if he was free to chat, he was about to embark on something else – whether it was watching *Neighbours*, having a bath or tucking into a plate of snails and garlic butter. 'You have quite a knack of coming at just the wrong moment,' he told me once. I annoyed him even more one day when I failed to wake him up to tell him that someone had called for him. Instead I took down a message saying that a certain well-known actor would call again. 'Have you any idea how difficult that man is to get hold of?' he shouted at me, extremely irate that I could do anything so stupid. He made me feel pretty ineffectual all in all and yet I appreciated his firmness. It was, as I have said, a bad time on the unit with some people struggling to come to terms with their diagnosis and others laid low by the relentlessness of it all. Bob's was a fresh and vibrant voice – though rather too strident at times.

I was surprised, therefore, that when I was finally able to speak with him he was relaxed and forthcoming. He told me how he'd gone to live in New York in the mid-seventies in the hope that his English accent would help establish his acting career which had never really taken off in England. This proved not to be the case and during the following ten years he only managed to get work on a few low budget B-movies. Instead he earned his living through restaurant work. Bob had always been philosoph-ical in his approach to life, so an AIDS diagnosis in 1989 following a bout of PCP did not unduly upset him: 'I don't know whether I was expecting it or not but I wasn't that shocked and I think I handled it very well. My friends and I all assumed it could get us because we'd done some pretty risky things. Of course we'd altered our practices as soon as news of this 'gay plague' came to our attention in the early eighties but a whole community doesn't radically alter its lifestyle overnight.'

Once diagnosed, Bob returned to England where he felt he would receive better health treatment from a more caring medical profession. 'I wanted to come home to roost. I wanted to die surrounded by familiar things and patterns.' Bob told me emphatically, and I believe he really meant it, that he hadn't once felt depressed about his condition. Although as a younger man he had suffered from repeated periods of depression, he'd had it all knocked out of him when he went through five years of therapy and later became interested in Buddhism and EST. 'I started off as a stalwart C of E – that crusty ridiculous religion – but in the seventies I started reading a lot about the Eastern religions and finally I did an EST training which turned my life around,' he said.

Another resident who shared a room with Bob thought his attitude towards AIDS was totally deluded. 'Who's he kidding?' this man said. 'No one can be that positive – it's not normal.' But that was precisely the point – Bob wasn't normal and while I came across people who were a little over the top in their complete acceptance of the disease and sadly often came crashing down to the ground when they no longer felt they had control anymore, Bob really seemed to be truly at peace with himself in the sense that although he kept fighting for life, he never resisted death.

Bob – who was so crotchety so much of the time – was full of praise for Lighthouse both in terms of its design and its provision of care. He was particularly compliment-ary about the attention that had been given to aesthetics, believing that the soft pastel colour schemes enhanced the environment and had a direct effect on his own well-being.

Of all the people I met with AIDS, Bob was the only one who seemed almost to relish his illness. 'I have no pain,' he said, 'I'm not depressed and I don't fear death. The parameter of my fear threshold is quite broad. For instance, in the past I used to test it by deliberately walking into the dangerous areas of New York late at night which I found really thrilling. Fear is not a weakness but I know it doesn't achieve anything. In fact, I find my enjoyment of the temporal plain is enhanced and I'd even say that as far as I'm concerned there are more positive aspects to AIDS than negative. I've got the sort of personality that takes what comes and then deals with it. I had so many changes thrown at me as a child that I got used to dealing with change in my environment very quickly. It was a great training for life.'

'But time is short,' I said, wanting to bring the subject back to the present and his own mortality. 'How much time is there?' he replied. 'Yesterday's gone and tomorrow's only a concept. It's the present that I'm interested in. It's called NOW,' and he clapped his hands loudly as if to squash a fly. These were words that pressed a button in me. I had always wanted to have that attitude instead of constantly harping back to the past or worrying about the future, but it was a hard state of mind to achieve even though I was a practising Buddhist. As if he had read my thoughts Bob said, 'No one said it would be easy.'

Bob was abrupt, direct and razor-sharp, as well as being funny and alarmingly perceptive. Once when I didn't know whether or not he wanted his meal brought to him and was loitering behind the curtain he yelled at me, 'Don't be so timid woman.' When I apologised, he criticised me for apologising too much. It drew me up short and made me think about my own actions. Was I being more self-deprecating and conciliatory than normal because Bob was dying of AIDS? I felt he understood me absolutely – my tendency to be unassuming, my fear of displeasing. When I left he thanked me for coming to talk to him, saying that he'd really enjoyed our conversation, and suggested I did an EST training.

Two days before Bob died he had a cocktail party to celebrate his birthday. It turned out to be a fitting final celebration to such a positive and original life. Although I was not there at the time I heard that he went to inordinate lengths to make it just as he wanted it to be. There was champagne and smoked salmon and the dozen or so guests who came crowded round his bed, mostly sitting on chairs which he had crammed into the tiny space. With so many actors present it was a lively and entertaining affair which led the other residents to retire behind their screens. His birthday party was his last social engagement, after that his diary was blank and as if he knew there was no point in prolonging procedures any longer, he suddenly became very weak and eventually faded out of life peacefully and painlessly, just as he had always intended.

I learnt a lot about AIDS from Bob and Jamie and, although their attitude towards the disease couldn't have been more different, both of them had a desire to make something good out of it. The difference was that Bob didn't want to dwell on the disease's progress in a medical sense whereas Jamie knew exactly what was going on in his body and was eager for as much knowledge as he could gain.

Because I was interested to know how people coped with the physical rigours of AIDS, I asked Jamie to tell me how he had been alerted to the onset of HIV and how it had manifested since his diagnosis. He was a very articulate man and, more than anyone else I met, was able to give me some idea of how it felt to be living with AIDS. He liked talking about himself but was worried that he didn't give others enough time or space to express their own feelings. In my opinion he worried unnecess- arily about this because although it was true that he could be long-winded and self-engrossed, what he had to say was never so introspective or egotistic that you felt bored or excluded. He was also extremely perceptive, as well as being sensitive to other people's feelings. For Jamie it all began in Melbourne, Australia, in 1988.

'The first sign was waking in the middle of the night drenched in sweat and although I managed to put it to the back of my mind I sensed that there was a dark cloud looming on the horizon. I said to a friend, "I've a feeling I'm going to get AIDS," but he only said, "Don't be ridiculous, you'll talk yourself into it if you go on like that." I was working very hard at the time and was conscious of putting an enormous depression on to the back burner which was probably all tied up with the virus starting to activate.

'The next thing that happened was that I started having major problems with my gums. I had to go to the clinic two or three times a week and the dentist had to employ special technicians to do deep-root cleansing. At the same time I was exhausted and didn't feel that I had an ounce of energy left in my body. The virus was obviously starting to go crazy, but because I had been offered a job in Sydney I made myself keep going. I was conscious that I was running on my second battery and needed to be kind to myself but I was excited at the prospect of starting a new job and meeting up with old friends again. Then, on the day before I was due to leave on the coach, I noticed a red spot the size of a pin head under my knee and I also started to get bad muscle aches in my legs. A few hours later I noticed that two more tiny spots had appeared which were itching like crazy. I wondered if it could be shingles but I immediately dismissed the idea and covered my skin with oils and creams in the hope that they would vanish.

'On the way to Sydney my leg began to feel even more achey and itchy so I took a look at it. In the space of twelve hours the spots had spread dramatically and I knew then that it was shingles for certain. But at that stage I didn't know that shingles was a manifestation of HIV infection, and I convinced myself it was all to do with stress. When I arrived in Sydney I was picked up by the friend I was staying with who drove me to her apartment where another friend of mine was waiting. This friend happened to be a doctor and I asked him to take a look at my leg. I remember the room went very quiet. He didn't say anything about my leg or about AIDS but just suggested I go to hospital first thing in the morning. That night I slept fitfully and had dreadful headaches because my eyes had become extremely light sensitive.

'The next day the doctor in the hospital took one look at my leg and confirmed that it was definitely shingles. I told him I'd been working very hard but he just looked really uncomfortable. Then he went out of the room for a while. I turned to my friend who had been with me all this time and I said to her, "You know what's going to happen don't you? They're going to come back and tell me I've got HIV." When the doctor came back he asked my friend to leave and when she'd gone he put his hand to his mouth and looked even more hesitant. So to help him out of his predicament I said, "It's OK, I'll make your job easier for you. I know what you're going to say – there's a possibility that I'm HIV positive isn't there?" He was a junior doctor and was having real problems knowing how to put it across.

'But he still didn't answer me directly, instead he asked me questions about my general health and about my lifestyle and I told him that I was certainly a high-risk case. Finally he said, "From what I can see there's an enormous chance you are HIV positive and in fact because of the shingles you'd be classified as ARC which means you'd have advanced HIV disease." He asked if he could take a blood test and of course I agreed. He said he'd process the test as quickly as possible but he wouldn't have the results until after the weekend. He also said there was a slim chance that this was not HIV and that I might simply be very run-down. Although I knew this was a very remote possibility, I clung on to it like a reed on water.

'The next day after a terrible night the shingles started

to ooze and blister. It had now spread from my heel to my buttock and half way round one leg. A few hours later I was back at hospital having a CAT scan because I had become delirious and so weak that I couldn't even lift my arms. They were worried that the shingles might get into my brain and give me meningitis.

'On the Monday morning the doctor phoned from the hospital to tell me that he was sorry but the result had been positive. I wasn't shocked at all and in a strange sort of way I felt relieved because I had such a bad neck and head ache that at least now I knew the reason for it. That evening there was a gay pride march which passed underneath our window. In the procession was a group of PWAs (People living with AIDS) and, as they passed, the crowd waved and went wild. As I watched this I felt my life being shot down with little arrows – it just folded up around me because I realised that these people had become my point of identity and from now on I would have to be affiliated with them. I don't think I've ever felt so isolated or so empty as at that moment.

'After a few days I started pulling back together. I was more lively and I could eat again so I decided I was well enough to start my new job. However, after just two hours of being there, I realised that I was still too ill to be at work and I had to leave and come home. I was desperate to be normal again but I hadn't given myself enough time to recover. Luckily, the firm were willing to wait for me and although my doctor told me I needed twelve weeks rest, I went back to work two weeks later despite still feeling weak and run-down.

'In the meantime I had been put on a massive dose of AZT. This meant that on top of all this I was also dealing with the toxic effects of the drug which resulted in nausea, extreme fatigue and severe muscle wastage. One of the

main problems was that I had to wake myself up throughout the night to administer the drug which needed to be
taken at three-hourly intervals. This, of course, totally
disrupted my sleep.

'The days were intolerable and I felt as if I was swim-
ming through wet cement. My way home took me up a
very slight hill and because I struggled to keep myself
together while I was at work, this slope, coming as it did
at the end of the day, became almost too much for me to
tackle and I made sure that everyone had gone on ahead
before I started my climb home. I used to grab hold of
railings to get to the top and more times than not
everything would buckle in on me and I'd collapse. I'd set
myself goals. For instance, there was an ice-cream stand
at the top of this hill which I used as an incentive to get
me to the top. But the trouble was that after a while the
ice-cream came to represent something unpleasant because
instead of it being a nice reward, it made me feel as if I
was being held down by something monstrous and by
eating this ice-cream all I was doing was filling up my
interiors which I began to see as cavernous. Finally they
cut down my dose of AZT and very, very slowly I began
to pick up again although I never recovered the weight
loss or muscle wastage.

'Nearly two years later I'd managed to save enough
money to pay for a flight back to England. I wanted to
come home because I felt there was unfinished business to
deal with over there and I wanted to tell my parents about
my illness. An old friend met me from the airport and I
was hoping to spend a few weeks with him in London but
then almost immediately I had a very bad bout of 'flu and
had to take to my bed for several days. Once I had
recovered I went to stay with my parents in Leeds but at
first was too weak and too tired to do any talking and

instead I hid away in an attic room and tried to regain some strength.

'My parents' reaction to my diagnosis didn't make me feel any better because after the initial shock, they did their best to bury it and pretend it wasn't happening. It made me realise that perhaps I had been wrong in trying to be frank with them. AIDS can be so unsettling for people's lives. Then, as if that wasn't enough, the depression I had been holding off for nearly two years suddenly decided to descend on me with a vengeance and I was immediately put on a course of anti-depressants. Also, I was constantly vomiting, which was very debilitating. I was staying with my sister at the time and it was very hard on her. She would spend all day lovingly preparing meals for me but immediately after I'd eaten them I'd just throw it all up. The fog in my brain was as dense as when I was first put on AZT and I once again felt as if I was wading through thick cement. I couldn't feel anything and I was incapable of making decisions. Eventually, however, I did manage to make the decision to throw away the anti-depressants and almost immediately I realised it was these pills which had largely made me feel so helpless and desperate. Slowly I pulled myself together and finally returned to London where Camden council eventually provided me with accommodation.

'Once I was in London I also made the decision to stop taking AZT. From the outset I had felt it was killing me and although the dose had been cut down from 1300 to 200 mils a day I still felt it was poisonous. Once I'd come off it, it took a long time for the toxic effects to wash through my system. I remember waking up about twelve weeks later and feeling strange. I couldn't work out what it was that made me feel this way but then I realised that for the first time in three years I was feeling refreshed and relatively lively. I'd forgotten what it was like to feel like this and it was a tremendous boost.

'Back in London I had a bad fever which doctors later thought may have been PCP. Also my guts were playing up and I was alternating between having chronic constipation and chronic diarrhoea. Then I started getting terrible breathlessness and a pain in my lungs which made me double up. I only realised something was seriously wrong when one day I collapsed in the street on my knees because the pain was so intense. I couldn't get any air into my lungs and I panicked. Once I'd recovered I went straight to the clinic where they X-rayed my chest and found that I'd been walking around for two weeks with a collapsed lung as a result of a pneumothorax which is when air gets into the pleural cavity. I went straight to hospital and they put tubes in my chest which were supposed to make it better but after coming out it happened five more times. For two weeks they tried to see if it would heal alone and for a while it seemed as if it might but then everything went haywire again and I was put back in hospital.

'Eventually after further unpleasant tests I was sent to a chest hospital where they removed part of the lung. That was the worst and most painful time of all. I felt as if I was being tortured because I had never experienced pain like it before and because they would never tell me what they were going to do next. The idea of being tortured proved rather beneficial in the end and I'm sure helped me survive because I kept wondering how strong my resistance was and how far they would go before I snapped.

'I have been fairly stable since then but I recently managed to sneak a look at a note written by my doctor and in it he said that my prognosis was very poor. Put so matter-of-factly like that, it gave me quite a turn. Now I feel I'm deteriorating fast because my muscle wastage has got worse and I weigh less than seven and a half stone. I'm also having problems with sores on my scalp, knees and elbows, as well as burning pains in my feet, and sometimes I have circulatory and vision problems. Recently I went back into hospital with crytococcosis which is like a thrush or candida which moves round the brain and if left untreated can cause meningitis. At one point I got very alarmed about my short-term memory and concentration and feared it might be the start of dementia, but thankfully that seems to have cleared now. I've also had to have several blood transfusions because I'm so anaemic – at one point I was having one every three weeks. I'm not sure whether the anaemia was caused by the AZT or HIV, or even by some of the prophylactic drugs I've been taking.

'All these ailments are a sign that the machine is going wrong and that messages aren't getting to my brain anymore but although I'm aware of getting steadily weaker I'm determined never to play the invalid. I've met too many people who lose themselves in HIV and eventually turn into the illness.'

· *Ten* ·

Where AIDS was concerned, confidentiality was crucial because imparting information into the wrong hands could so easily sabotage people's lives. At London Lighthouse, confidentiality – in the very strictest sense – meant not telling anything to anyone about anybody, and those who breached it were either reprimanded or dismissed. I found it a difficult and inaccessible issue since the boundaries were so blurred. It was not something you could lay down guidelines for since barriers were constantly being built and rebuilt.

As far as I could see, breaching confidentiality was a little like breaking the speed limit. On a very minor and fairly harmless level it happened fairly frequently and was impossible to police. Some people thought Lighthouse was too preoccupied with this issue and far more paranoid about it than actual service users were. There may have been some truth in this but an organisation like London Lighthouse had to be single-minded in its commitment and determination to ensure that confidentiality was never broken even if it did mean that some people's attitudes were unnecessarily rigid. For instance, when a member of staff bumped into a volunteer on holiday, both of them tactfully avoided the other's gaze. It seemed strange to me that they could not even greet each other just as friends or acquaintances, simply omitting to say where or how they had met.

Everyone I spoke to agreed that confidentiality was extremely easy to break. When I was redirecting mail to residents who had already left the unit, I had to white-out the name and address of London Lighthouse in case anyone other than the ex-resident saw where the envelope had come from.

Once, when I was on the residential unit, I asked a nurse about a certain resident whilst still in earshot of another resident. The nurse said nothing but then beckoned me to one side. Instead of reprimanding me for attempting to break confidentiality, he put it very tactfully by saying that he made it a rule never to talk about one resident in front of another one. I felt very stupid and wished that I'd thought before opening my mouth, but the question had seemed so innocent at the time.

And there was another occasion I nearly slipped up as well. I had been sitting in the cafe having lunch with a few friends when someone I had worked with many years ago came up and tapped me on the shoulder. I was so surprised to see him that, before I had time to think, I found myself asking him what he was doing there. This was not a question you should ask anyone who walks through the doors of London Lighthouse and I only did so because of my delight at seeing him after so many years. Luckily, he didn't seem to mind my intrusive line of questioning and told me that he had recently moved into a flat round the corner and frequently came to Lighthouse for lunch.

One volunteer who had been working at Lighthouse for two years wrote about his experience of breaking confidentiality in *Highlights*, the Community Service newsletter:

'My knuckles were recently rapped by a senior member of staff at Lighthouse. Rightly So. But it hurt. I certainly learned from the experience, and I hope that other volunteers may also benefit from what happened to me. It concerns the question of confidentiality, which has always seemed to me to be more complicated and more difficult than it is sometimes presented as being. I think I now have a much deeper understanding of the issues involved.

'What happened was that I was told in the presence of three other people that someone who works at Lighthouse was seriously ill. I then passed this information on to someone else with two other people within earshot. At the time it seemed to me that the two situations were comparable. All the people involved work at Lighthouse. But there was a significant difference.

'On the first occasion all the people present were from the same department. On the second occasion the two within earshot were from another department, and that made all the difference.

'I am privileged to work in three different departments at Lighthouse: the residential unit, day care and centre support services. In all the teams in which I work, it is necessary to share information about service users. But that information should be confidential to that team.

'The reasons for confidentiality are, I should hope, well known and well understood. It should not be necessary to elaborate on the stigma, discrimination and hostility that exist in relation to HIV and AIDS. It is in the practical application of confidentiality that problems sometimes arise.

'In a sense my mistake was to see the whole of Lighthouse as a safe environment in which information could be shared without any harm ensuing to the person concerned. No doubt it is. But I had missed the point. I had failed to appreciate the individual's right to control her or his own life and to control information relating to it. I had no right to assume that the person concerned would want everyone at Lighthouse to know. No right at all. And sore knuckles are a small price to pay for what I have learned.'

Some people were well versed at respecting confidentiality. A worker in Home Support Services told me proudly that a woman being supported by Lighthouse had come to stay on the residential unit for three weeks respite care and that the news had taken ten days to filter through to the department. Although this sort of strict adherence to confidentiality was admirable, sometimes it seemed to foster a kind of detachment, in which people were not talked or thought about, and perhaps were not visited or rung up, because the people who knew they were unwell felt obliged to keep the information confidential.

One person I came to know on my induction course and whom I liked very much suddenly wasn't to be seen round the building anymore. When I asked people who worked with him where he was, no one would tell me and since he'd been pretty disgruntled with his work as a volunteer at Lighthouse, I automatically assumed he had packed it in. Subsequently, however, I discovered that he'd suddenly been taken ill and had died just a few weeks later. Whilst understanding that no one had the right to disclose information about another person, I couldn't help but feel annoyed about it as I was certain this particular person would have wanted me to know what was wrong with him. He was a shy man who did not find it easy to reach out and ask for help so information from him was bound to be unforthcoming. I wished I had been told, if only to have been able to ring him and tell him that I was thinking of him. I wondered if this was an unnecessary restriction of communication and an example of how confidentiality could be imposed on someone who actually would have wanted people to know more about their condition.

There was also a feeling among some people that by putting such a strong emphasis on confidentiality, it only succeeded in adding to the atmosphere of secrecy. Barriers would never be broken and society would never accept people with AIDS as long as so many feared revealing their status. Even in a relatively safe environment like London Lighthouse there were very few of the workforce who made public knowledge of the fact that they were HIV positive. But one of those who did told me: 'I don't mind who I tell and I won't lower my voice on a bus if I'm talking to someone about having the virus because I feel that at least this is something I can do to help people get used to the idea that AIDS concerns them too. While I acknowledge that confidentiality is vitally important to people with AIDS, the outside world won't get to grips with what it's all about if we all remain anonymous.'

Perhaps Father John White, an Irish Roman Catholic priest who was the Pastoral Care Co-ordinator at Lighthouse, was the bravest of those I met who had spoken publicly about having AIDS. I considered him brave because not only did he have the Catholic Church to contend with but also his family who were part of a culture which didn't recognise the existence of such a disease and subsequently were unable to offer those who had it any support.

'London Lighthouse reminds me of the Catholic church,' Father John told me when I asked him about the organisation for which he worked. 'There's lots I find difficult about it and yet I'm still a part of it.' He played an invaluable role – providing pastoral care, conducting services (as well as empowering people to conduct their own) and doing outreach work with Christian and Jewish groups. He described Lighthouse as a garden and said that his position would always be on the borders. It was not a matter of regret or concern because in his view someone had to be on the edge.

Father John was someone it was impossible not to like. He was tall, bearded and in his early forties, with warm eyes and the gentlest of smiles, who almost always wore a T-shirt and jeans. His was a late vocation, having trained as a psychiatric nurse before deciding to become a priest at the age of thirty-one. He belonged to the Irish Kiltegan missionary order, though he often felt isolated within the Church.

I liked him particularly, although I never got to know him well because he was always in a great hurry as well as being in great demand. He was different from most people who worked at Lighthouse. For a start he had a visible religious faith, and he was neither so political nor so loyal to the organisation that he would not openly find fault in it. Tokenism, for instance, worried him and he wondered if he would have been chosen for his job if he hadn't had HIV. The affinity I felt towards him may have had something to do with his religion. Though I had been a practising Buddhist for nine years, I was brought up as a Catholic and I felt very at ease with him. Apart from that it seemed to me that he had a sincere, generous, non-judgemental attitude, as well as a great sense of humour.

Father John had been working as a missionary in Kenya for ten years when in May 1986 he went to Nairobi for tests after suffering from a rare type of pneumonia. The test revealed that he was HIV positive and, on discovering this, he immediately decided to leave Africa and come to London for further tests. It was in London that he came in contact with Lighthouse through attending counselling sessions with John Shine and later he ran his own support group, after training as a volunteer.

Initially on coming to England he worked as a hospital chaplain in Slough and as a curate in West London but he did not tell his colleagues or family about his status. This proved to be a huge weight on his mind. 'I knew that it was an added burden for me but I could not envisage what it would be like working with people who knew. I felt it would be an unfair burden for them to know and that it would be easier for me to deal with it myself. I can now say with hindsight that it was not the way to do things. The way to deal with HIV is to talk about it and be upfront about it – in other words to face the challenge. Being HIV positive is a new sort of challenge with which to live. However, being open about it with people who will accept the situation and will be supportive makes living with it much easier.'

When he finally told the local bishops, he received the reaction he had long expected. 'They thought I should give up work and be taken care of, in other words be put down like a dying dog.' Telling his family was even more difficult because they had no idea how to deal with it and consequently didn't manage to deal with it. They reassured themselves with the fact that he looked well and one of his sisters tried to encourage him by saying, 'It will never happen to you.' When he was in hospital suffering from suspected PCP another sister asked him how his 'cold' was because she couldn't bear to acknowledge that it might be something more serious. Father John described this as part of the denial process: 'It denies the reality of the situation and it takes away the freedom of the person to be ill or even to die. I have seen the same type of attitude towards people with other terminal illnesses. The patient can accept it and cope with it but the family denies it so that the patient often ends up supporting the family.'

He was clearly a man of immense bravery because in 1989 he publicly declared his HIV status on Irish television, despite numerous emotional pleas from his family not to. 'I did the interview,' he said, 'because I felt that, by my silence, I was actually colluding with the oppressive silence that surrounds the whole issue of AIDS within the Church, especially in Ireland, and also in the Irish culture. Irish PWAs here in England feel that they cannot go back to Ireland or their families because of that attitude. Some families do come here to visit and support the person with AIDS but there is no source of support for them back in Ireland. Even when their son or daughter has died, the family refuse to face the reality and so they go back and tell their friends and neighbours that he or she has died in a road accident or from leukemia. Months later, they will ring us up in distress wondering why they still feel so badly. They are not aware that it is because they have not yet faced the basic reality and truth.'

Father John would never say how he got AIDS: 'People cannot understand how I have AIDS because I am a priest – but the answer I always give is that I got it because I am human and AIDS is merely a virus which attacks humans. There's no point in trying to put labels on people, saying that they're homosexual or drug addicts. Going around with a tattoo on your forehead saying "I'm gay" may be a form of self-victimisation. It's not so much out of curiosity that the people want to know how you got it, it's also to make a statement about themselves and tell everyone that they are not in that category. They say AIDS only affects people who are from Africa or gay men, and so by categorising people through the labels they wear they can discount them. None of us should ever do that. People can talk all they like about how I got AIDS. It had nothing to do with Africa. I could have picked it up there, or it could have been a long-term thing.'

In November 1989 Father John hit international news headlines when he challenged the authority of the Church during the Vatican's first conference on AIDS by demanding that the voices of people with AIDS be heard. No one with AIDS had been allowed to speak at the conference and the implicit message seemed to be that AIDS was a result of 'God's wrath'. Cardinal John O'Conner of New York urged a return to moral values and reiterated the Church's stand against prophylactics to prevent the spread of the virus. 'Good morality is good medicine,' he said and talked of a ban on the use of condoms in trying to slow down the spread of AIDS. He referred to assisting people with AIDS to die, but never of helping them to live. 'The AIDS-infected will no longer be "productive" in social terms,' he said. 'Their quality of life has deteriorated to a point at which their lives do not merit prolonging.'

After having listened to four hours of such oppressive language, Father John could hold back no longer and he unfurled a prepared banner which proclaimed 'THE CHURCH HAS AIDS'; he was referring to the body of the Church, in other words its members, and implying that if one part of the body had an illness then all the rest of it must also be affected. Then he stood up and declared in front of an audience of priests, bishops and nuns: 'I am living with AIDS and I have no voice at this conference.' Within minutes he was seized by Vatican security guards who after trying to discover if he really was a priest expelled him from the building. The protest, however, created such an impact that within hours delegates had raised a petition of hundreds of signatures in Father John's defence.

Outside the building Father John mounted a five-hour vigil during which many delegates came out to congratulate him and show solidarity. The following day the President of the conference, Archbishop Fiorenzo Angelini, personally invited him back to the gathering and in a contrite show of forgiveness embraced him warmly in front of the whole conference. The Church had obviously not anticipated such an angry protest from one of its own kind, but nor had it expected so many delegates to rally in his defence. It was a fruitless conference which ultimately did little more than allow theologians and AIDS researchers to exchange already preconceived views.

Father John often talked publicly about his status and his feelings of brokenness as a person and as a priest with HIV. He felt saddened that more priests could not come forward to identify themselves to one another as a means of creating some kind of mutual support. 'I know I am not unique – I know there are others. I know of some with whom I have spoken on the telephone or with whom I have had indirect contact. I know through other people of priests who have died of AIDS-related illnesses but it has always been kept a secret. I feel very alone in the sense that it is like becoming part of a ministry and feeling I am the only one in it. Some priests must be terrified of my openness about the issue because what I'm doing is opening a whole can of worms which they're trying to keep firmly closed. But the can of worms we fear when looked at is often found to contain precious gems.

I had been working as a volunteer at London Lighthouse for several months when I myself spoke out publicly in a way which was to change my relationship with the organisation and deepen my understanding of HIV and AIDS.

'Avoid any satellite projects,' one journalist friend warned me when I broached the subject of possibly writing a book about my experience. He meant don't simultaneously write any articles for newspapers or magazines because it could jeopardise the project by antagonising staff and thus spoil the fragile relationship that had built up between myself – as the writer – and Lighthouse as the subject of the book. But when I was given the opportunity to write a piece for the *Independent* about my week as a volunteer on the residential unit, I ignored these words because I had nothing critical to say about the establishment, on the contrary what I had seen so impressed me that I could not imagine how I could possibly antagonise the individuals concerned. Nevertheless I checked the copy with London Lighthouse's press officer and though in retrospect I can see that he was not wildly enthusiastic, he endorsed it with the proviso that I made a few changes and omissions. This I duly did and two days later the article appeared taking everyone at Lighthouse by surprise.

I was working nights at the time and that evening as I cycled up Ladbroke Grove something inside me began to sound alarm bells and I started to feel a little nervous. In the standfirst at the top of the piece the *Independent* had added these words: 'Marina Cantacuzino spends a week with AIDS victims.' The word 'victims' troubled me. It was a word which had been used unsparingly by the press since AIDS was first howled across the front pages of our newspapers. Despite NUJ guidelines which discouraged usage of the word, it was still frequently to be seen even in quality papers like the *Independent*, as was the even more divisive and discriminatory term 'innocent victims', which refers to haemophiliacs and children, and which singled out gay men and drug users as the guilty transmission groups.

Of all the terms used to describe people with AIDS, the word 'victims' was most deplored at Lighthouse, but there were other words which also caused offence. 'AIDS carriers/HIV carriers' was thought to encourage discrimination and victimisation because it described people who were HIV antibody positive as presenting a risk to others. 'AIDS sufferers' was thought to be inaccurate since many people with HIV were healthy and happy and even people with AIDS experienced long periods of relatively good health. 'AIDS cases', often used in an epidemiological context, was seen as dehumanising because it emphasised the disease rather than the person.

In the eyes of AIDS organisations it was the media who had created this language of blame. Geoff Warburton who joined London Lighthouse as a member of staff in July 1986 believed that with there being more knowledge and less confusion than in the early days, organisations like Lighthouse should develop better ways to challenge offensive, irresponsible and oppressive journalism.

He had thought long and hard about the language of AIDS and had developed a paper entitled 'AIDS and Language: Guidelines for the Press' which he paraded like a banner in front of any journalist who dared set foot in London Lighthouse. These guidelines were rarely followed however. But Warburton, in the process, came to realise that not all articles that used the word 'victim' were necessarily bad, ill-informed pieces of journalism. Like others whom I met at Lighthouse but who preferred not to voice their opinions too publicly on such highly contentious matters, he began to wonder if he had become a victim to the word victim. For how many of us would object to being called a victim of a crime such as theft or rape? And were not people with HIV and AIDS victims just as much as anyone else who had faced disaster in their lives?

Warburton said: 'I began to realise that being a victim does not exclude one from having the usual range of human characteristics which may include empowerment, dignity, joy, anger, determination and blue eyes. It is when we label someone as just a victim and attach the connotations such as hopelessness and powerlessness that we are being oppressive.'

I was right when I imagined that the word 'victim' would not exactly endear me to those readers affected by HIV and AIDS, but I was wrong when I thought the rest of the article would manage to placate them. I considered my article to portray a positive image of Lighthouse – something which was badly needed following a highly critical piece that had appeared in the *Independent on Sunday* the previous January revealing complaints about the way Lighthouse was run, and which had shaken the confidence and morale of the entire organisation.

As I walked into the building late on that Thursday night, I knew instantly that I had ceased to be a liked and trusted volunteer and instead had become an unpopular and unprincipled hack. The reception staff greeted me coolly which filled me with dread and forewarned me of the atmosphere that lay ahead. As I climbed the stairs to the residential unit, my legs felt heavy; every part of my body was trying to pull away from a situation that I knew I had to face.

The article consisted of a small, edited section of my diary which I had kept from the first day of working at Lighthouse. It was unsentimental and unsensational, but described exactly what I saw in terms of the effects of some of the illnesses which people with AIDS suffered from. It was a description of my week, seen through my eyes and written in my words. And in my naïvety – as well as in my vanity – I thought the workers and service-users of Lighthouse could not fail to approve of it. As it happened, however, a large majority were outraged by my audacity at having written about something which, as a relative newcomer, I was ignorant of and therefore could not possibly portray with any degree of accuracy. So, having been trusted and respected, suddenly overnight I became one of the most unpopular people London Lighthouse had yet encountered.

Night duty always had a tendency to drag, but on that night especially the minutes ticked by with a terrible relentless monotony. It wasn't exactly a cold shoulder I received on the unit, it was genuine dismay at the fact that they hadn't been consulted or forewarned. No one had advised me to ask the nurses on the unit to check over my copy, though I subsequently realised that it was an unfor-tunate omission on my part. The only excuse I could find was that I genuinely doubted whether the article would ever see the light of day.

Another complaint was that because the article had appeared so near to the events that I had described, certain people might have been able to recognise themselves or might have been recognised by their friends and if this happened it would amount to a breach of confidentiality.

I sat and listened to all this in a state of complete disbelief – sick, humiliated and terribly disappointed. Lighthouse had become a place of immense importance to me. I found my work there rewarding, educative and stimulating. I had grown fond of the people there, and most of all I believed in it as a model of care and as a place which was slowly, perhaps imperceptibly at times, changing the attitudes of the world around us. Suddenly to have betrayed the organisation and committed such a base and treacherous crime, by insensitively writing about people without their permission and in a way that might identify them, appalled me and sent my confidence and self-esteem crashing to the floor.

Worse was to come. The next day I discovered that it was not only the nurses on the residential unit who were indignant about my article but the entire organisation – service users, staff and volunteers alike. With them, it was not so much a question of having possibly broken confidentiality since only those working on the unit were able to identify the people I had written about, but a question of appalling journalism. I had done what hundreds had done before me: by describing the raw details of illness I had shown people with AIDS to lack dignity and had therefore dehumanised them. I had shown Lighthouse to be only a place of suffering and death, rather than also a place of love and joy and I had written the article in a distorted and egotistical manner by putting myself, rather than the nurses or residents, at the centre of the picture. I think some people failed to appreciate that the piece had been called 'my week' and not a week in the life of the residential unit.

Twenty-four hours after the article appeared, I was summoned to attend a meeting with two senior members of the staff. I was certain I was going to be jettisoned from the organisation and was therefore much relieved when I was treated with respect and a certain amount of compassion. The fact that I was clearly deeply dismayed and upset by the depth of hostility felt towards me made them see that strong words would have only been counterproductive causing me to topple further under the weight of such harsh criticism.

The accusation of having betrayed their trust was somehow the worst to bear. I was told that people who were about to use Lighthouse services or people who had been recently diagnosed with HIV or AIDS would be filled with fear after reading my article. I had apparently shown people with AIDS to be powerless and had described only the most gruesome aspect of the unit – in other words there had been too much emphasis on vomiting, diarrhoea, brain lesions and dementia.

While accepting that the balance had not been exactly right, I did not entirely agree with everything that was being said. I felt there had been some humour in the article, a certain directness and some lighthearted comments about food and the role of volunteers, but at that point I was in no fit state to argue my case: I was convinced that I had entirely misjudged the situation and somehow got swept along by some of the more underhand methods of my profession – namely to distort and sensationalise. One senior member of the management team did say that she thought the tone of the article probably reflected the shock I felt at what I had witnessed. There was certainly some truth in this, but when she said it was a shame that I hadn't shown a warmer picture of the unit by also mentioning some lighter scenes, such as people opening a bottle of wine and having a good time together, I could only answer, quite truthfully, that I hadn't written about such things because I hadn't witnessed them. Indeed, several nurses had commented on the fact that the atmosphere on the unit during those weeks had been particularly grim. Later that was to change and I witnessed some far happier times.

At the end of this gruelling session I was asked to

accompany the nurses to the cafe for a cup of tea, paid for by Lighthouse (which was a rare privilege), so that people in the building could see that I was still accepted at a senior level. Christopher Spence kept well out of the fray. I heard on the grapevine that he had said 'It's by no means the worst article we've had written about Lighthouse,' and I took this to be my first show of support.

But my position was not yet restored and the days that followed were some of the most painful that I have had to live through. Not only was I facing a wall of hostility – mostly unspoken but sometimes voiced in a venomous and underhand manner – but I was also doubting my skills as a journalist as well as my compassion and sensitivity as a human being. Even though friends and acquaintances outside Lighthouse reassured me that they had found the article human, factual, sensitive and powerful, it gave me little comfort because these were people who knew little about AIDS and were entirely removed from its world. All that mattered was the fact that I could have hurt and offended people with AIDS and I longed, more than anything, to be able to turn the clocks back.

Just as you are advised to climb back on a horse after falling off, I knew the only way to confront this problem was to keep going back to Lighthouse no matter how rejected I felt. So during the week ahead I went in every day in my endeavour to make peace. In the short term it would have been far easier to run away and never go back, but in the long term I knew that for my own sake and for the sake of those I had offended the matter had to be resolved. I had created this mess and I had to clear it up.

Some volunteers were very angry with me as well. An extremely caring and gentle woman, who worked on the unit three days a week, looked at me not with anger but with sheer disbelief: 'How could you do it?' she said with tears in her eyes.

It was the reaction of Julian that probably hurt most of all. Julian was a man living with AIDS and also a fellow volunteer on reception. I had always enjoyed the days I worked with him because of his sharp humour and sense of fun. He was very popular at Lighthouse having been brought to the unit two years previously suffering from encephalitis and had not been expected to pull through. His fight to survive and his return to leading a near normal life epitomised the indomitable spirit of living well with AIDS which was the undercurrent of Lighthouse's philosophy. Julian was the sort of person who was incapable of showing anger in an aggressive manner: he made a joke of it instead.

Two days after the article had appeared, I was walking down the corridor when I heard him say very loudly to the other people he was with: 'Oh no, here comes the renegade.' I shrank away but later called him to one side in order to apologise. On seeing my eyes fill with tears, he expressed surprise: 'Goodness,' he said, 'I didn't know you were sensitive.' But that was half the trouble, I was sensitive, and felt these accusations cruelly.

It was like a grieving process, with my love for the people and the place having been taken away, followed by rejection and then a feeling of total despair. I was still reeling from the shock of this, but also trying to find my feet again and construct from the mess that I had created a new and different relationship with Lighthouse. Looking on the positive side, I could see that the experience had also provided me with what would hitherto have been impossible – namely an insight into what people with HIV and AIDS have to go through when they are ostracised by their community or place of work.

Julian was as angry with me as he was capable of being angry, but it didn't take long before he was offering me support, showing some surprise when I told him that people outside Lighthouse had viewed the article in a very different light. He then took it upon himself to find other people in the building who were still seething over what I had written, so that they could hear from my own lips how I had not come to Lighthouse with the prime intention of stealing a story, that I had not meant to harm or antagonise them and that I was repentant to the point of wishing I could retract the whole thing. I felt as if I was on trial and during my trial Julian spoke in my defence. It was a remarkable show of generosity and forgiveness on the part of a man with AIDS who had found my article inaccurate, negative and dishonest, and whose anger I felt was more than justified. That evening, before leaving, I saw Julian and kissed him goodbye. It was the first time since I'd come to Lighthouse that a kiss had felt real and meaningful. I cycled home up Ladbroke Grove feeling my spirits had been lightened just a little. Although I felt just as damaged by gnawing feelings of shame and regret, Julian had shown me a hint of light at the end of a very dark tunnel, and it gave me hope.

It transpired subsequently that the nurses felt less hostile towards me over the article than people in the rest of the organisation. Pete, the nurse, said that the reaction was typical of people who didn't work on the unit and who didn't know what it was really like up there. Two residents had died at the time of publication and he was angered by the fact that people were wasting more energy thinking about an article in a newspaper than about the fact that two more lives had been lost.

AIDS was an emotive issue and feelings ran high at London Lighthouse. I was told by several people that

overreaction was not uncommon and that small organisations coping with the pressures of growth were inevitably
oversensitive to criticism. As the days went by I no longer
saw the article in the entirely negative light that it had
been painted to me in. The voices of critics are always the
most vociferous, and I discovered that not everyone felt
outraged by what I had written.

Forty-eight hours after the article first appeared I was
still being eyed with suspicion. Though some people had
decided to forgive me and had now condescended to speak
to me again, the underlying feeling remained that I was
someone who had betrayed their trust. That afternoon I
bumped into Sam. He kissed me warmly, as he always
had done, but instead of being heartened by his embrace,
I shrank away. Sam was a volunteer who only worked at
Lighthouse two days a week and so I assumed he had not
yet read the article and therefore knew nothing of the
ensuing row. 'So, you haven't read it then,' I said,
resigned to the fact that I was about to face another hostile
reaction. 'Of course, I've read it,' he said, 'what's the
matter? I thought it was fine.' When I told him what I had
been through during the past two days he was appalled
and kept repeating, 'But we're supposed to be a caring
place?'

In fact, the incident over the article had repercussions
that went far beyond what I could ever have imagined and
on a personal level penetrated the defensive shell which I
had unconsciously constructed around myself. Getting to
know Sam – who was to give me a great deal of support,
never once hesitating to stick his neck out in my defence
– showed me exactly how caring people at Lighthouse
could be. I had managed to stir up deeply felt emotions
and understood the animosity people felt towards me, but
in doing so I experienced a new level of friendship which

involved love and commitment and made the whole upsetting episode ultimately extremely valuable and worthwhile. There were, however, one or two people who after that were never able to accept my presence at Lighthouse, but being in such a small minority they never bothered me very much.

I had always thought of my time at Lighthouse as a journey and as with any journey there was a point when I began to feel alien and alone in this strange country, longing for the safety and comfort of my own familiar world. Over the incident of the article I had reached this point, but getting to know Sam put me back on course. I felt I had turned the corner and was finally able to scrape my self-esteem back off the residential unit's floor. Out of everybody that I met at Lighthouse, Sam was the person I came to feel closest to. I established an intimacy and a love for him which went far and away beyond anything I had imagined possible from my work as a volunteer at Lighthouse. As a perfectly healthy man with HIV, he was someone who was living his life courageously in the shadow of AIDS and whenever I was with him I too felt the coolness of that shade.

Criticism of the article came from near and far – including other parts of the medical profession who were always eager to find fault with the way the residential unit conducted its affairs. I was amazed when I was told that one passage particularly had been thought to show the nurses in a poor light. The passage read:

I am walking down the corridor with three others
when Tim, who has dementia, opens the bathroom
door with his trousers around his ankles. 'You with the
curly hair,' he shouts at me, 'come in here.' He is
insistent and for a moment I wonder how far the duties

of a volunteer go. Thankfully, a nurse is at hand and discreetly disappears with him into the bathroom.

This apparently had been further evidence that nurses at Lighthouse were never at hand when needed. I was astounded when I heard this criticism levelled at the nurses as I had felt quite the reverse – indeed the nurse in question had arrived instantly to help Tim gently and unobtrusively out of a predicament and to rescue me from a difficult situation.

Two things happened after this which finally made me able to forget the whole episode and realise that, though I had certainly made errors of judgement in writing the article, in no way could it be condemned as a wholly negative and inaccurate piece of writing.

The first episode was comparatively insignificant but it changed the situation entirely by showing me that there were different ways of seeing things. I was standing in the queue of the cafe one day when a man I had never met before, wearing brightly coloured cycle shorts and carrying a helmet, tapped me on the shoulder. 'Are you the woman who wrote that article?' he asked.

My heart sank – not only was I having to put up with criticism from people I knew but now from perfect strangers as well. Resigned to yet another attack, I told him that, yes, I was the writer. But his reaction, like that of Sam's, was totally unexpected. He told me that he thought it was the best article he had ever read on the subject of AIDS. As I stood there in total disbelief, waiting to catch a note of sarcasm in his voice, he went on to say that he had found it 'real, honest, and unsentimental'. Then he thanked me three times for having had the courage to write it.

I later discovered that he was a man living with the

virus who occasionally volunteered at Lighthouse and who was involved in a number of support groups. Here, at least, was someone with HIV who had been affected positively by what I had written and who had responded in the way that I had intended. I wanted to hug him but I was so stunned by what he had said that I simply stood there without saying a word.

He also said something which showed me that nothing anyone said was ever the whole truth, but rather a partial truth, just as my article could only ever hope to be a partial truth. He referred to the one line in the article which had caused most offence. I had quoted one of the nurses saying that she had had so much diarrhoea to deal with that day that it had been 'running through the corridors and down the stairs'. I was accused of portraying the nurses as flippant and uncaring and showing people with AIDS to lack dignity and have no control over their lives. The man in the cycle shorts, however, said he thought this was the most powerful and moving metaphor of AIDS that he had ever read.

The second episode was more important. A little after the furore had died down, John Shine – who had heard of the trouble I was in and had read the article – sent a letter to the press officer at Lighthouse, asking for a copy to be sent to me. I had barely heard of the man at this stage, other than knowing he had been involved with setting up the project from the beginning. In the letter he said that he thought the article was a very good account of a period on a unit caring for people with HIV and AIDS, and went on to say:

> In my observation there is an unspoken code that says don't talk about the difficult side of HIV disease, that it is only appropriate to talk about 'people living well

with AIDS'. With the mortality rate still running for nearly a decade at around 50 per cent, those experiencing wasting, memory loss, disfigurement, disability or who are dying, are often left feeling somehow that they have failed or are not doing the right thing. This subject is often the content of counselling sessions. Peter Randall, the founder member of Body Positive, coined a phrase that sums it up, 'the tyranny of positive thinking'.

When I met John Shine later he told me that he thought the article had acted as a catalyst for people's fears, and in so doing had raised people's awareness. It had been seen as negative because it focused on death and people feared dying. He believed that some people at Lighthouse were in danger of succumbing to this so-called 'tyranny of positive thinking' which didn't allow for people's fears and vulnerabilities.

Another early pioneer of Lighthouse, who left the organisation shortly after its official opening, told me that he believed Lighthouse had become a part of our death-denying culture because its staff were not adequately trained in dealing with death. 'Lighthouse would only change this attitude if its volunteers and workers began to deal with internalised misinformation about death and oppression,' he said.

This he felt had not yet been done. He illustrated his point by telling me that when a friend of his had died on the unit, all that the family had been offered as solace was a glass of whisky. He felt that 'this collective internalised ignorance, or lack of awareness' was reflected throughout the organisation. This was a man who like other early pioneers believed that Lighthouse was going to be the first place to make enormous inroads into the collective consciousness, but when this dream proved to be unattainable, he became aggrieved and disappointed.

Having worked on the unit for some time I did not feel this criticism was justified. I couldn't really see how offering a glass of whisky to someone who had just been bereaved was an example of our death-denying culture. I had seen nurses spend many hours with the relatives, friends and partners of people who had died. I had read a thick file full of letters thanking and praising nurses for their help.

Also, it seemed to me that while some people certainly put too much emphasis on living well with AIDS, the organisation fought daily with trying to find a balance between upholding life while not ignoring or avoiding death. At times it was accused of colluding with the pretence that death was not the natural and healthy conclusion to life while at other times it was accused of being morbidly obsessed with dying. For instance a recent AIDS newsletter had taken Lighthouse to task for enforcing an HIV=AIDS=Death conspiracy in its preoccupation with death and dying under the chilling headline 'Deadly Counsels: the Necrophiliacs of AIDS'.

Christoper Spence was painfully aware of the difficulty of sustaining the balance to reconcile attitudes to life and death. From the beginning London Lighthouse had often been attacked both for supposedly imposing the tyranny of positive thinking and for being over-preoccupied with death, both of which were obviously occupational hazards. 'Paradoxically I believe true empowerment lies along a narrow ledge,' he once wrote, 'one which each of us must find for ourselves in our own way at our own pace, perched somewhere in the gap between these two giant shibboleths.' On another occasion he added that to the extent that any organisation is a microcosm of the wider society, Lighthouse inevitably internalised the denial of death prevalent in the wider society. However, it seemed to me that this issue was being addressed by numerous means – in direct care, counselling, staff training, the staff support system, team building and stress management programmes, as well as in managerial supervision, in the after-death service and funerals, in recent quilt-making sessions and in support groups for the bereaved.

John Shine believed it had been largely due to his desire to talk openly about death, and his belief that the fear of death could be confronted only by accepting it as a reality, that eventually made his views incompatible with many gay activists working in the AIDS field. In the early days he recalled everyone being much more open about death and it was in this climate that he wrote an article which told of the death of a man he had cared for. Months before I had even heard of John Shine I came across this article, tucked away in a file in the Lighthouse press office. It had impressed me so much that I copied it down line for line. In writing about Graham, who had Kaposi's Sarcoma, Shine said:

> It is ironic that a man who put so much store by his looks should end up with such a disfiguring disease which caused more lesions on his face than there was normal skin . . . He was able to die in the comfort of his own home, surrounded by the very people he always wanted to be there when he died. We set the room up with candles and incense, and played music that he liked very much. We had made up beds all around Graham's bed, for his friends to sit or lie on. By this time he was unconscious, but very peaceful, and we were explaining everything to him as we went along. His friends enjoyed taking part in his nursing

care and his mother never left his side. She lay next to him on the bed all through the night. He died so peacefully that it was hardly noticeable. We just stayed with him: there was nothing more to do. The candles burned on, the music played on and people cried. After some time, his friends helped me to wash him and lay him out. We laid him in the centre of his double bed with two soft toys, one each side of his head, which were gifts he cherished. His mother came back and people took turns to lie next to him, love him and say goodbye.

He concluded the article by saying: 'Helping Graham to die so well has been a pleasure and a privilege.' Although Spence had encouraged Shine to write the article and had indeed been present at Graham's death, Shine believed that this article marked him out as someone whose approach to death was radically different to that of the rest of the organisation.

Society's view that AIDS was a death sentence had understandably a lot to do with the fact that more and more emphasis was being put on challenging, surviving and living with AIDS. To concentrate on death therefore was giving voice to negative thoughts and some people took it to be a sign of failing in the fight against this controversial disease. Shine was aware of how much denial still existed: 'I'm not criticising that,' he said, 'there are times when denial is a very appropriate thing, but too much of it leaves people very confused and worried because it means they're walking up a blind alley.' He believed that only by working with that fear could people carry on with living.

In his essay 'Reclaiming the Power' Christopher Spence wrote: 'AIDS has made me lead my life as I'd want to lead my life,' and this philosophy pervaded London Lighthouse with its emphasis on living and dying well with AIDS. Some people who worked there and others who used its services talked about Lighthouse with the passion and conviction of someone recently converted to a new philosophy or religion. It was to the organisation's credit that it had been able to have such a radical effect on some people's lives, but on the other hand, not everyone was capable of or even wanted to use AIDS as a springboard for positive change.

The philosophy of Lighthouse was based on the premise that you could change your life, and that life-threatening events were an unexpected opportunity to do so. Hamish McGregor, the Training and Organisational Development Consultant, believed that the key word was sensitivity when it came to trying to implement the vision of AIDS as 'an opportunity, individually and collectively, for transformation'. 'It's very arrogant if we feel we can change people's lives. We don't have the right. If people want a hand we can do that, but if people don't want to change their lives we've no right to impose it on them. I know some people who feel guilty because they feel compelled to lead a permanently healthy existence and that feeling of compulsion has put them under a lot of stress which of course is totally counterproductive.'

Counsellors at Lighthouse told me that some service users found the philosophy of the organisation a rather bitter pill to swallow. One counsellor, who had worked there for two years said that some of the people who came to see him had said, 'AIDS is dreadful. I'm not grateful, I don't feel it's a great opportunity for making big changes in my life and I just wish that someone would acknowledge that fact.'

This then was the result of the 'tyranny of positive

thinking'. I had indeed met a few people who admitted to being exhausted from the punishing schedule they had set themselves – for instance taking endless vitamin pills, sticking to a stringently healthy diet, having acupuncture, reflexology and aromatherapy sessions, going to counselling and support groups, keeping fit and regularly attending drop-in centres. John Shine had noticed during his many years of counselling people with AIDS that a common cry was, 'I'm knackered but I have to keep going with all these things otherwise I won't survive.' The feeling was that if you could maintain a positive attitude, then you would keep well, and this of course left little space for negative feelings. Although no one was denying that people with AIDS felt sad and angry and sometimes even died feeling that way, the implication was that to be in this state of mind too much of the time signified failure.

Another issue raised by my article in the *Independent* was how explicit to be when telling the world about the sort of debilitating, degrading illnesses caused by AIDS. A number of people told me they felt AIDS had become sanatised in the press and because of that no one took much notice of it anymore. Because I had been extremely literal in describing what people had to endure in the way of losing control of their bodily functions, I was accused of having shown people to lack dignity and therefore of having dehumanised them. I could never quite come to terms with this criticism or see how someone suffering from chronic diarrhoea should lack dignity. Did the Kurdish children poisoned by water contaminated by Saddam Hussein lack dignity because television pictures showed them defecating by the side of the road? To me these children, like the men and women at Lighthouse who were dealing so bravely with such dire afflictions, demonstrated precisely what dignity was all about.

Philip Sanderson shed some light on why there seemed to be such a fear of showing the disease as it was: 'There's a stigma around chronic illness,' he said. 'People think if you make HIV nicer than it is, so that people all die with love and dignity and don't become undignified because they've lost control of their faculties, then people will be more accepting of AIDS. We at Lighthouse haven't decided whether to be collusive with that or to challenge it and become hard hitting. We're frightened we'll lose the vision statement if we show how much anger there is around. It would be much better for people to look at the nasty side of this disease because it would help people to refocus on what HIV is really about. We need to shock and anger and put London Lighthouse back into the forefront of criticism.'

· *Eleven* ·

Since London Lighthouse's opening in 1988 nursing there had changed with an increased need for intensive rehabilitation and convalescence reflecting the changing dynamics of HIV. Earlier diagnosis and better treatments meant that people were living longer. In the early days many people died of PCP because the symptoms (a dry cough and shortness of breath) weren't detected in time. But there was a sinister side of this changing pattern, for as people with AIDS managed to fight off illnesses like PCP and cryptosporidium, their bodies were becoming infected by more virulent and obscure opportunistic infections.

The shift from acute illness to chronic illness meant that in some ways there was more suffering than in the early days because although people were living longer, their level of health was fairly poor for many years. In Lighthouse I noticed that many people needed crutches or wheelchairs which I was told had not been the case two years ago.

Although 95 per cent of the nurses on the residential unit found London Lighthouse an enlightening and supportive place to work, there were a few exceptions. One nurse who had left before my involvement began said she went because she felt policies weren't keeping apace with social and medical changes. Her main criticism was that the unit had become an unsafe place to work because of an increasing number of residents with drug problems. Violent and abusive behaviour had been rare in the early days when the majority of the residents were articulate, middle-class men, but increasingly and necessarily the beds were being occupied by people who lived on the margins of society and who had little emotional or financial support.

There was a drug policy being drawn up around the time of her departure but she felt it had come too late, and her main criticism was that management had no idea of the risk that nurses ran. 'This place was started by people who believed that it should be a safe place for people with AIDS, where residents would be free from cruel and censorious behaviour. But what about the nurses? It's certainly not a safe place for us anymore.'

Few nurses felt as strongly about this issue as she did but most acknowledged that the unit was not always a 'safe' place to work. At times the philosophy of adopting an unjudgemental attitude meant that residents had the right to behave as they pleased. A charge nurse told me that residents would come from hospital where they hadn't been listened to and so once they got to Lighthouse they felt they could behave exactly as they pleased.

Philip Sanderson knew that interaction between the different types of residents on the unit was sometimes difficult and occasionally even dangerous. The dynamics he felt were tremendous, and potentially explosive, and he knew that something needed to be done to improve the safety of the staff. In his view there would come a day when management would have to turn round and acknowledge that they'd tried to give all people equal access but failed. By the summer of 1991 the access was somewhere in the region of 15 per cent women, 10 per cent drug users and the remaining 75 per cent gay men.

The residential unit had already received more than it's fair share of criticism from other health services, some of which was justified but most of which was simply straightforward professional rivalry. This was bound to be the case in such a young and experimental organisation which was attempting to provide a new kind of working environment – namely comfortable and non-institutional surroundings, adequate support time, a substantially higher salary then in any NHS hospital, and no obligatory uniform. It had frequently been remarked therefore that nurses at Lighthouse had an easy time of it, dressing in jeans and T-shirts, taking home good pay and sitting around drinking cups of tea all day while chatting to residents.

Everyone who had worked on the unit had experienced criticism of one kind or another, whether from the media, other medical bodies or from former colleagues. Philip Sanderson, who was never one to be daunted by adversity, saw it all as a healthy exchange of views: 'The day I stop being criticised about the strategy of care in the residential unit,' he told me, 'will be the day I've colluded with them or become complacent.'

The most virulent critics tended to be people who had never used Lighthouse services but who had heard about other people's bad experiences on the gay grapevine. Certainly not all residents were satisfied with the way Lighthouse operated but a large majority had nothing but praise for the organisation and its nursing staff. The criticisms I did hear, therefore, were few and far between. One woman said she found the freedom and non-structure of Lighthouse too difficult to cope with and she wished she could be given more attainable goals. Another man described the place as a 'trendy Auschwitz' because there were all these fit and healthy people running the show, looking after all the frail and immobile residents. And away from the organisation I met a number of gay activists who deplored the management hierarchy and the 'classism' at Lighthouse and who said they would 'rather die in the gutter than go there'.

Some people with the virus stayed away from Lighthouse because they were afraid of what they would see. Even if they had a friend who was seriously ill they would avoid the unit making elaborate excuses as to why they were unable to visit. The question they couldn't face addressing was: 'Am I really going to be like this one day?'

Although the residential unit was an important part of the integrated model of care at Lighthouse, the nurses remained separate from the rest of the organisation, isolated geographically at the top of the building, as well as by the nature and structure of their work. Apart from residential volunteers and residential unit assistants, only the caretakers wandered through the unit freely: even workers from the Community Services department, who may have had one of their service users staying on the unit, had to seek permission for access.

One nurse believed that the unit needed to become more of an integrated part of the whole because it meant that only the nurses, volunteers and residents really knew what was going on up there. 'People downstairs work with and see people who are living with AIDS but a lot of the people we are working with are dying.' He had been particularly angered by an incident which had taken place in the cafe: 'I was having my half-hour lunch break with several other nurses when a man sitting on the far side of the room suddenly vomited. Everyone looked embarrassed and no one knew what to do, so they looked at us because we were the nurses and we were the ones who were expected to deal with things like that.' He had also known residents who would not eat in the cafe because they felt intimidated by such a lively and sociable place. In their wheelchairs and dressing gowns they felt conspicuous and out of place next to the many young and fashionable people who ate there.

When the fire alarm went off accidently one afternoon it graphically illustrated the sort of isolation sometimes experienced by residents on the unit. Not knowing whether this was a genuine or false alarm, volunteers rounded up the eighteen mobile residents and escorted them down the fire escape while the nurses stayed behind with two residents who were seriously ill and who in the event of a real fire would have had to be carried to safety. When everyone who had vacated the building had gathered in the carpark, it became apparent that this was a false alarm and people relaxed a little and started laughing and joking. The cold and weary residents, however, were largely ignored by the rest of the staff as they waited for nurses and for wheelchairs to take them back to the unit.

The nurses at London Lighthouse did not wear uniforms. This was to help break down the barriers that existed between nurse and patient in NHS hospitals and so that people with HIV and AIDS shouldn't be singled out by the very fact that they were the ones in civvies. Sometimes it caused confusion. One resident whose initial visit was in the first months of Lighthouse's opening told me that at first there were a lot of complaints from residents who couldn't distinguish between doctors, nurses, domestics, volunteers and fellow residents. He admitted, however, that although he found this annoying, there was also something rather appealing about the confusion, 'because it meant we were all alike'. Later it was agreed that anyone who worked on the unit should wear a badge with their first name printed on it as a means of quick and unintrusive identification.

Unlike in the NHS I saw no hierarchy on the unit. The two doctors who had an office on the first floor outside the unit were called when needed and much of their work was taken up with assessments and admissions. In hospitals care is given out by the nurses but directed by the doctors, whereas at London Lighthouse there was a multidisciplinary system, with nursing-led care and a free interchange of ideas between all professionals involved. Lighthouse operated a team nursing system whereby all the nurses were divided into three teams and thus able to provide continuity of care.

It also meant that residents got to know the people working in their team and began to feel a part of that team. Julian, who stayed for a second time while I was working there, and who hadn't been back since 1989 when he was brought in with encephelitis, requested that on his return he should be looked after by team B again although many of the original nurses had left. It was a way of working which most nurses found satisfying because it meant being in control of a particular resident's care, while also being able to consult their team.

The residential unit was not like an acute medical ward in an NHS hospital, nor was it a hospice for the dying. It offered both respite and palliative care while continuing to liaise with other medical staff and health authority professionals involved in a person's care. The aim was to complement the existing statutory services, not to take over or replicate them. Philip Sanderson thought that, although a certain amount of experience in AIDS was important and necessary to the job, it was something that could be acquired through training and working on the unit and was not a prerequisite for employment.

He believed that equally important to having good nursing skills was the ability to communicate with residents and colleagues on a human level. 'I have been criticised for bringing in someone who had just done a "Back to Nursing" course and who hadn't done hands-on nursing for ten years but I employed her because of her life experience and the quality of her work in the local community,' he told me. He also believed in getting nurses to 'use their humanity'. This meant acknowledging that they felt hurt, vulnerable and threatened and not exercising their power. 'Nurses in the NHS like having that power because it stops them feeling vulnerable and frightened and anyone who encourages them to give control back to the resident is a big threat.'

At Lighthouse control was given to the residents, instead of being taken away from them. For this reason people who come to stay on the unit were called residents and not patients. At first I occasionally blundered by referring to residents as patients. Language and terminology at Lighthouse were important. I heard of one man who had been castigated by his boss for calling people 'dear' and referring to women as 'ladies' as his attitude was deemed to be old-fashioned and patronising.

One of the first nurses to work on the residential unit told me that when she came to Lighthouse she was impressed by its ability to give people space, privacy and choice, although she also found it difficult because she had been trained to give out directions. 'I realised how little I had really communicated with the people that I cared for and it was very difficult learning to talk to people as people rather than as patients. I let myself open for a lot of vulnerable things and felt very unsafe because people came and asked me a lot of tricky questions about lifestyle, death or care and I couldn't give them the pat answers I was used to. I had to be honest and open and that was very hard.'

Pete came to work on the unit in 1989 after finishing his training in an NHS hospital. He had no experience of AIDS, but was disillusioned by a system which he believed promoted hierarchies and left patients ill-informed. He was appalled at how doctors and nurses tended to project their own morals on to patients. 'Seeing how the NHS operated made me realise that if I was going to make a career out of nursing then I had to be careful and put myself in the position of the person I was looking after by treating them in exactly the same way I'd want to be treated.' Lighthouse, he felt, had given him the chance to do just that.

'But my ignorance really worried me at first. After the induction course I knew a little bit more but there seemed so much to learn. I was shocked by the residents as well because I'd only seen people look that emaciated in a geriatric ward. At the beginning I made sure I didn't cry and I kept my distance because my professional training had told me that was what you did in distressing situations.

'Then after about four months I was looking after a fellow who'd lost all his friends through AIDS and whose parents didn't want to know him anymore. He had reached the terminal stages of the illness and he had no one to be with him, so I sat with him one Monday night until he finally died at four o'clock in the morning. I had no one to ring because there was no one to tell so I went out into the conservatory and unexpectedly just burst into tears. Another nurse could see what was going on and she followed me. She offered me a cup of tea, and I said, "thank you" in a very clipped way. Then she said, "It's OK to cry, you know." So I did, I wept buckets and I felt a lot better for it.'

For a nurse to be involved was not seen as a weakness at Lighthouse. It was all part of the philosophy of care which believed in treating residents as friends, and if not as friends, then at least as equals. Some residents were having to face not only the social stigma of AIDS but also the reality of their own impending mortality and sometimes nurses were the only people they could talk to. They were often the same age, from the same peer group, and so personal identification was not difficult.

The capacity that some nurses had to become involved in residents' lives amazed me, but this committed, and sometimes intense, relationship between nurse and resident could make the unit a very hard place to work. One nurse told me, 'The day it doesn't upset me anymore will be the day that I won't want to do this kind of work anymore.' Nurses stayed for an average of eighteen months because of the dangers of burn-out, and support groups, supervisions and study days were available on a regular basis as a means of relieving the pressure. One of the few nurses who had remained at Lighthouse since it opened told me she was still amazed at what a supportive place it was. 'I'm allowed to be upset about someone and show how I feel, but I've also learnt during my time here to step back when I feel I'm getting too involved and say to myself, "I like this person very much, but I'm not in love with them."'

Most nurses had to find coping strategies with which to distance themselves emotionally from the relentless nature of the disease. I watched many nurses helping a resident get over an infection successfully only to be faced a few weeks later with the same resident, but a different infection.

Pete told me of one resident who had stayed four times. 'When he first arrived he had HIV-related dementia, he was incontinent and could only answer "yes" or "no". His mother had been looking after him and been quite distraught until a friend told her about London Lighthouse. When he was admitted he began to take AZT which had a positive effect on his dementia. We all felt wonderful about him because at least here was someone who looked like he was going to die but made a remarkable recovery. After that he'd come in to visit us and he was very proud because he was able to look after himself again and he had even started to drive again. But slowly things deteriorated once more. He started falling over and they discovered he had a lesion on the brain. Eventually he was paralysed from the neck down and he came back to Lighthouse, this time to die. He used to be a singer and we'd spend hours in his room singing songs. We all loved him and he loved us.'

Pete was extremely aware of how easy it was for nurses to misuse their position of power. I had only ever had experience of NHS hospitals as a patient and at first I wondered whether it was really possible for nurses to have equal relationships with the people they were caring for, when those people were weakened and debilitated by ill health and dependent on their services. I wondered too whether some residents didn't actually rather like handing over responsibility in a place which would protect them from careering down hill.

Pete was sure it was possible because it was all about handing power back to the patient. In other words, residents on the unit were expected, if well enough, to make their own beds, to decide when and where they wanted to eat and at what time to take a bath or shower. If they didn't like it on the unit then no one made them stay. If they wanted to sleep together then that was fine too. I remember once I arrived and the futon room was occupied by two residents who by 10.30 still hadn't emerged. Since the room was needed for a massage one of the nurses had to knock on the door to wake them up. Later in the kitchen one of them, looking a little bashful, confessed that he had been giving the other man support in the way of touching and hugging, but nothing had happened sexually. He didn't need to look bashful, however, since there were no rules at Lighthouse about residents not having sex with one another. The only rule was that they shouldn't upset or offend anyone else.

When the unit opened in 1988 it was seen as one of the primary ways in which Lighthouse could put its philosophy of empowerment into practice. If someone had not wanted to be turned in bed, the nurse would probably have said, 'OK, it's your decision, we won't turn you.' However, it soon became clear that there had to be a balance between empowering the individual and maintaining the nurses' professional status, and consequently by the time I arrived at Lighthouse things had become much more proactive. Rather than allowing a resident to have full control all of the time, nurses now kept control of certain areas and saw their role more as one of supporting an individual in the choices he or she might make.

Philip Sanderson remembered that 'in the early days if someone was mobile we'd tell them to self-medicate because that was what they'd have to do when they got home. But we soon realised that that was a cop-out because we still had power over the residents because we were the ones who decided whether or not that person should be in control or not. Nowadays when a resident

arrives a nurse will spend at least half an hour with him
finding out their objectives for the next three weeks. What
we say is, "I'd like you to be self-medicating by the time
you go home, but you can do it in stages and we'll help
you."'

In March 1988, Christopher Spence outlined the objectives of the residential unit in an article written for *Midwife
Health Visitor*:

> The only hope for people with HIV and AIDS is a
> holistic response in which they are assisted by prac-
> titioners in all branches of medicine and health care to
> consider every aspect of their health and well-being and
> to take back full responsibility for it. In order to be able
> to offer such assistance, we, as practitioners, need to
> break out of our narrow professionalism, to listen well
> and to learn from each other as well as from people
> with HIV and AIDS.
>
> To do this is to strike a blow against the blind and
> sometimes I believe fatal assumption that AIDS is an
> automatic death sentence. It is to make a significant
> contribution to a healthy shift in the balance of power
> in relationships between health professionals and
> patient, and to promote a fuller understanding of the
> connection between self-image and the functioning of
> the immune system.
>
> By common consent, acute beds in general hospitals,
> even if they were in ample supply, are not suitable for
> people who are in the closing, and often protracted,
> phase of their lives. Such wards are structured towards
> people getting well rather than the different ethos of
> caring for the dying.

When a colleague with the virus became sick and moved
up to the residential unit the mood of the whole building

and the morale of staff and volunteers noticably altered. We all knew people who had the virus and we all hoped it somehow wouldn't happen to them, so when it did it was especially shocking and sad.

One nurse described caring for a colleague as 'horrendous and heartbreaking'. The dynamic of a relationship inevitably changed when a nurse had to become involved in the care of a colleague who would often also feel uneasy about the sudden change in roles. It is not surprising therefore that when some volunteers and staff became ill they preferred to go elsewhere. Others, on the other hand, adapted well and found that Lighthouse provided everything they wanted in terms of respite and palliative care.

There was one nurse on the unit with the virus who was prepared to identify himself to me. It can't have been easy for him caring for people who were mirroring illnesses that he himself might one day develop. Unlike most of us who could be pretty confident that we were not going to suffer in such a terrible way, nurses with HIV lived with the probability of this one day becoming their reality. Although the same holds true for all Lighthouse volunteers and staff with the virus, the nurses were seeing, experiencing and involving themselves closely in the lives of people with AIDS in a way that was not required of other workers.

I met Richard on my first week as a volunteer on the unit. He was in his early forties, had been diagnosed HIV positive in 1988 and was working part-time as a nurse. He was gay but refused to think of his sexuality as an issue. 'I'm not a gay man,' he would say, 'I'm a man who happens to be gay,' and he felt uncomfortable with gay activists since he had never experienced gay oppression. He did not broadcast the fact that he was HIV positive but he made himself available to any resident who needed to talk to someone with a more direct understanding of what it was like to have the virus.

Once I saw a resident break down in tears because he felt so awkward and ugly next to his nurse who was a healthy and attractive young man of twenty-one. He resented the way his nurse talked about what he was going to do at night the men that he was seeing, and the holidays he was planning. Someone like Richard, therefore, provided an important antidote in a world that could easily have become a 'them' and 'us' situation.

Through talking to Richard over the months, I learnt that he had taken two years off after his diagnosis in order to adjust and settle into a new way of life. Then in 1990 he came to work at Lighthouse because he felt he had a resource to offer. Like a good many of the people with the virus who work at Lighthouse, he chose to have the test because he wanted to be in control of his life. At the time of his diagnosis health professionals had moved away from talking about high-risk groups and instead were talking about high-risk behaviour and since he'd been involved in high-risk activities, he knew he would most probably prove to be positive.

Despite having the maturity to put himself on the line and find out the truth, receiving the result came as a severe blow. He described the shock as I heard it described many times: 'I didn't hear anything the doctors were saying to me. I just sat there unable to move, feeling the blood drain from me.'

By the time I met Richard he had developed a coping mechanism of switching off, though he was never able to do that completely and his HIV status always lingered at the back of his mind just like waking in the morning with the knowledge that something unpleasant has happened the night before but you can't remember exactly what. 'I sometimes wonder if I have blinkers on and I'm not facing up to the fact that this has something to do with me,' he said. Some other people I met who were living with the virus, but were still asymptomatic, amazed me by saying that sometimes they didn't think about it for days on end. This degree of detachment I would not have imagined possible. Philip Sanderson, for instance, told me that he didn't even associate himself with having HIV: 'I know it's pure denial,' he said, 'but it's a comfortable place to be and I'm staying there.'

Richard hoped and at times believed that he could avoid the fate of so many others. With the medical profession predicting that nearly all people with the virus would go on to develop AIDS, this seemed naïvely optimistic and Richard knew it. 'There probably hasn't been one person in any of the twenty-three beds here who hasn't at one time thought "I've got a chance",' he acknowledged ruefully.

Richard spoke in glowing terms of his partner who also worked at Lighthouse and who also had the virus. His first reaction to his partner applying for a job at London Lighthouse had been negative. 'I didn't think he should pursue this type of job considering his HIV status. We had both only recently been diagnosed and it all seemed too much too soon. It would mean HIV becoming his world; he'd be surrounded by it at work and then he'd bring it home with him where we already had it and where we were only just starting to deal with it. It took me a while to feel happy with the AIDS connection and it wasn't until two and a half years later that I felt I wanted to apply for a job at Lighthouse. I spent those first two years doing up houses and selling them because I wanted to be on my own and work through some of those early issues away from the pressure of a career. Eventually, however, I realised that this wasn't enough and I needed the stimulation of working with people and meeting people.'

Richard and his partner seemed to have an exceptionally supportive and caring relationship and were referred to by one member of staff as 'the perfect couple'. They were both convinced that had one of them tested negative, difficulties and jealousies would have arisen, whereas their common fate had had the effect of tightening and securing what was already a very deep bond.

I liked Richard the best of all the nurses I met because he was one of those rare people who could instantly make you feel not only welcome but also valuable. The resident-ial unit could be an intimidating place for volunteers to work. The intensity of the nurses' work and the close relationships they formed with each other meant that for new volunteers it was easy to feel isolated and underused. I certainly felt this at the beginning of my time there, and later too when I could only work one five-hour shift a week and discovered that this was simply not enough to get to grips with what was happening on the unit. The fast turnover of residents and staff meant that for me as a volunteer continuity was lacking and each time I went in it was as if I had to start all over again.

Volunteers on the residential unit were expected to do a wide variety of tasks – such as running errands, answering telephone calls, collecting menus and taking meals to residents, loading and unloading the dishwasher, ironing, talking and sitting with residents, accompanying residents to hospital appointments, and sometimes if volunteers had some basic nursing skills hands-on work as well.

It was not by general agreement the easiest place for volunteers to work and the fact that some volunteers came just once and never returned was proof of this fact.

Everyone – nurses, volunteers, the volunteer co-ordinator, and even Christopher Spence himself, agreed that certain things had to change before a volunteer felt really comfortable and welcome on the unit. To say that all volunteers had felt uncomfortable would be very misleading. There were those (almost all of whom worked at least two or three shifts a week) who found it a thoroughly rewarding experience, but others, including myself, sometimes found it a very difficult environment to work in.

It was mainly I think the large number of people working on the unit and using its services that made it so difficult. When I was only working one shift a week it meant that every time I came many of the residents and nursing staff would have changed. Another problem was that nursing staff were trying to function normally despite a 7 per cent vacancy rate and consequently were tired and overworked. Sometimes it seemed as if a volunteer was just another person to get in the way.

The responsibility, of course, largely lay with the volunteer. Working on the unit and getting the most out of it depended to a great extent on using your initiative and being assertive, but sometimes I found it a fairly intimidating and exclusive place to be since the staff were so obviously running the show. The very nature of their expertise excluded volunteers from their work.

There was occasionally some friction between staff and volunteers on the unit. Though I never witnessed any myself, I heard of one or two nurses whose attitude towards volunteers was considered inappropriate. Most of these nurses, coming from NHS hospitals, were not used to working with volunteers and felt that they shouldn't be privy to certain information. There was a file for each resident with their medical notes and although these files were often left lying open on desks it was forbidden for volunteers to read them and none, as far as I know, did or indeed particularly wanted to. On the other hand, there was also information about a resident which could prove extremely helpful to a volunteer's understanding of the situation and given that all volunteers were trained to understand the importance of confidentiality it seemed only sensible that they should be told as much about each resident as possible. With nine out of ten nurses this was never a problem, but just occasionally there were those who called their colleagues aside to have a quiet word out of earshot of the volunteer.

This was never an issue on day care where I was told by the volunteers who worked there that they were always included as part of the team and expected to take part in all the feed-back meetings. This was largely because day care had been set up with volunteers as integral to the service whereas with the residential unit volunteers had been brought in rather as an after-thought.

The situation on day care was also much more conducive to this kind of team work. For a start there were only five staff members and far fewer service users who came in on a regular basis. Even if a volunteer worked just one shift a week he or she would come across the same members of staff and the same service users every time, thus making it much easier to build relationships and acquire some continuity to their work.

I think my main disappointment ultimately with the unit was that I didn't always feel very useful. Whether this was because I didn't make myself useful or because no one made much use of me, I'm not entirely sure, but one thing I'm certain of is that to have had just a little more direction, information, feed-back and words of encouragement would have made the world of difference.

I should also emphasise that these problems were being addressed at the time by volunteers and staff alike in a new monthly meeting which was an attempt to thrash out the issues and find a better way of working together. No one was to blame. It was simply the nature of working on a unit which cared for people with AIDS and was too often understaffed.

· *Twelve* ·

London Lighthouse was born out of a desire to create, among other things, a place where people could die well and be supported to engage in the process to the full and to remain in charge of their lives in every way possible. In 1987 Christopher Spence said: 'People have two fears. The first is the fear of death. In my experience it is easy to create a sufficiently safe climate in which people can face their terror of death and let it go. But second is the fear of a bad death. Eventually the issue is not whether we die – or even when we die – but how we die.' He went on to talk about a friend of his who had died of AIDS and who during the last ten days of his life had been in a hospital ward, ready to die, but having to endure the indignity and discomfort of a ventilator that was needlessly prolonging his life: 'To die like him in an acute-care setting is an offence. The whole culture is not set up to really think about the distinct needs you have because you're dying.'

At the time the hospice movement, which historically had cared for people dying of cancer, did not feel equipped to cope with AIDS. Underlying that was the fear among staff of the disease itself, plus anxiety over losing urgently needed revenue, since the movement was funded largely from conservative sources. An alternative to an acute-care setting was to die at home with unpredicatable domiciliary services at your disposal. Lighthouse was set up to offer the very best possible palliative care conventional medicine had developed, while at the same time being committed to a holistic approach and offering as many complementary therapies as possible.

Although methods may have changed since Lighthouse opened, the philosophy of care remained the same with people's autonomy upheld and their right to say 'I want to die now' respected. The aim was that someone should be given good pain and symptom control with the minimum aggressive medical treatment. One man I witnessed at the terminal stages of the disease was having terrible diarrhoea from the drugs he was taking and was very distressed by the constant badgering of needles and drips. In the end, encouraged by his partner, he took the decision to stop all medication, and he died five hours later – probably a day or two before he would otherwise have died. Stopping all forms of medication, however, did not necessarily mean that someone would die more quickly and could indeed create further complications followed by an uncomfortable death. If this was the case then empathy and discretion were necessary in order for nurses to make the right decisions. I knew one man who asked his nurse again and again to have his catheter taken out but in the end the nurse took the decision to leave it in because she believed the catheter would cause him less discomfort than having to die soaked in his own urine.

Another difficult part of the work on the unit was that nurses were expected to look after the living as well as those who had just died. In NHS hospitals once a patient has died nurses will have little call to see the body again. On the unit, however, a nurse's involvement with a resident continued until the body left the building sometimes several days later. It was the nurses' job to lay the body out in the room where he or she had died so that friends or relatives could take their leave without feeling that everything had to be tidied away around them. After several hours, two nurses would then take the body down to the mortuary and place it in one of the fridges. During the next few days they might have to return to the mortuary several times to lay the body out for friends and relatives in a small room, furnished much like any other bedroom at Lighthouse, but kept unheated. In some ways this continuing contact with a resident was very rewarding but it could also be extremely stressful and some nurses never got used to it.

In 1986 when the plans for the building were drawn up, AIDS was talked about as an epidemic which would kill tens of thousands of people, so, when the residential unit opened, a mortuary with fifteen sections was developed to cope with this anticipated demand. But up until the time I left Lighthouse the maximum number of people in the mortuary at any one time had been five – and this was mainly due to delays in funeral arrangements.

Jennifer, one of the charge nurses, used to work on the Thomas Macauley AIDS ward at Westminster Hospital. Although she admired the sort of acute treatment that the NHS were able to offer, she had felt frustrated that a shortage of beds meant little provision was made for the terminally ill. Lighthouse, with its person-centred philosophy, inspired her and she applied for a job as a primary nurse. She got it and eighteen months later she still claimed to get a kick every time she walked through the door. To illustrate the extended role of a nurse at Lighthouse she told me the story of Philip, a man she had cared for during his stay, and someone whom she had grown extremely fond of.

'He was a flamboyant gay man, proud of his sexuality and proud of the fact that he'd shaken hands with Princess Diana and Princess Margaret. He was one of the first people to be treated with AIDS at St Stephen's Hospital and had had a multitude of infections. He'd been written off a number of times but had always bounced back. His condition was deteriorating, so he came to Lighthouse because he felt at home here and loved the people. He didn't arrive thinking he was going to die because he was never one to give up hope but we knew he probably would.

'He had unrealistic expectations about his health and while he was here we had to help him face the fact that he was dying. During the last days of his life he had severe generalised pain throughout his body so we gave him morphine and he finally lapsed into unconsciousness. Friends came in and played music and washed his mouth with whisky because that was his favourite drink and his mother washed him with the help of an Anglican priest who was also a friend. When he died he had all his family and friends around him. He'd made preparations for his death and discussed the outfit he wanted to be dressed in and he looked stunning. We all stood round the bed, holding hands and talking about him. It was beautiful and natural and very, very sad.

'That evening on my way home I bought a record which I knew Philip had liked and I danced to it and thought about him. Philip's mother found it quite difficult to leave the building. She wrote to me a few weeks later thanking me for allowing her to wash her son. She said it had been very important to her because she'd washed him as a baby, and now she'd washed him as a grown man. She also asked me if she could come and see the room where Philip had died just so that she could see for herself that he wasn't there any more. So two months later she came down to London, I showed her the room and we had a few tears together. Then we had lunch and talked about Philip for an hour and a half. She also told me she'd written to Princess Diana to say he'd died and had received a handwritten letter back and a bouquet of flowers.'

Getting involved in the dynamics of the family and spending time with bereaved friends and relatives was all part of a nurse's work on the residential unit and I witnessed many occasions when a lover or a worried parent would ring up for comfort and reassurance, often because they'd returned to a community where they couldn't talk to anyone about their sick or recently deceased child. It wasn't uncommon for a resident to ask a nurse to explain to his parents, who might not even know that he was gay, what was wrong with him and why. Sometimes those relatives had no idea what London Lighthouse was and required a great deal of support when they found out.

As a result it was not unusual for some nurses to become as involved with a resident's partner as they did with a resident. The room with the fold-away futon bed had accommodated many friends and relatives from around the world who came to Lighthouse to be close to the person they loved. Bereaved partners and relatives very often wanted to keep in touch with nurses because they formed the last link with the person they had lost.

This letter, written to 'the loving caring staff at Lighthouse', sums up how many parents must have felt:

This letter is dedicated to you all, from us, in showing us such courage and dedication, love and compassion, at the extraordinary circumstances which we found at the Lighthouse. It has been a revelation, an enlightening experience which we shall never, ever forget, to know how much H was cared for and treated with such tenderness and love, that words seem inadequate to try and thank you all.

We are naturally in a deep state of shock, still, and the grief will continue for a long time to come at H's loss, but because you have helped us face the truth in such a way as to make the pain at least a little more bearable, we can only praise you all, at such humanity you have shown us.

We are both deeply, deeply moved,
God bless you all.

There were, however, some residents who never had visitors, not even during the last hours of their life. Because AIDS affects such young people most residents had parents who were still alive, but rejection was not uncommon in a disease linked with sexuality and drug abuse. When a resident had no visitors, the nurses and volunteers often became that person's sole means of support.

Occasionally, however, residents who came in for respite care wanted to shut themselves away from the world, to be left alone to curl up and die. I met one such man on the unit. His name was Maurice, he was in his late forties, and the only person who ever visited him was his cousin from Yorkshire, though in the end Maurice forbade even him to come to Lighthouse, saying they had nothing in common anymore. His mother had died when he was a teenager and he hadn't seen his father for fifteen years.

When I first met Maurice it was thought he might get better and go back to the flat that he shared with his ex-partner, even though the relationship had soured and both men could no longer stand the sight of each other.

Maurice was a man tormented by guilt. In all the time I worked on the unit I met few people so distressed and so unable to come to terms with his illness and his sexuality. But, despite this, he had a very active mind and was always interested in what was going on in the world outside. He often used to ask me about Buddhism while I in turn asked him about Catholicism. It was when he no longer made the effort to talk and no longer displayed any interest in what was going on around him that I realised he'd lost the will to live.

One day I was passing his room when I heard him calling in anguish, 'Hello, hello, can you help me?' I ran to his assistance but it wasn't a volunteer or a nurse that he wanted. It was God. Not knowing really how to handle this I went to get one of the volunteers who was a nun. Later in the week I kept hearing him call, 'Dear Jesus Christ help me, help me. Where are you, dear Lord?' It was a pitiful sound and although much effort was made to provide Maurice with the pastoral care he so badly needed, nothing seemed to sooth his troubled mind.

After several days of crying out for God, he stopped eating. One of the last meals he ate was a bowl of semolina which I fed to him very slowly, a teaspoonful at a time. From the few conversations I had with him I learnt that Maurice had studied theology at university, had wanted to be ordained, but then changed his mind at the last moment and become a teacher in a boy's prep school instead. He regretted terribly having come out in the sixties because he felt it had encouraged him to adopt a very promiscuous lifestyle which he now held responsible for his present predicament.

In his confused state of mind he no longer had any faith in the abilities of an intercedent such as a priest but instead believed that he himself somehow possessed a hotline to

God. The fact that he was unable to make contact made him distraught and because of this he began to spit out his medication and refuse drink. In the end he deteriorated more rapidly than anyone had anticipated. He was transferred to a low air-loss bed and plugged into a pump which gave him regular doses of diamorphine and anti-sickness drugs, since a side-effect of diamorphine was nausea.

These anti-sickness drugs had the double feature of also being a sedative, so all in all at the end of his life Maurice was pretty comfortable. His nurses would turn him every two hours and wash him at the same time; they put drops in his eyes to make them less red and sore, and they arranged for a priest to give him the last rites. He was slipping into unconsciousness when I last saw him, though he was still just able to grimace and groan a little. One of the nurses said, 'He's still his old self, I see,' as she tried to administer the eye drops and he pushed her hand away.

When I returned to the unit the following morning I found a candle burning on the desk at the nurse's station and in the office, written on the noticeboard, were the letters 'R.I.P.' with Maurice's name and underneath the date on which he had died.

I was asked to clear his room of possessions. Normally a friend or relative would have done this but in Maurice's case there was no such person. All that remained of his physical presence was a touching collection of objects – potent reminders of his tragically empty life. There were a few 'get well' cards from ex-colleagues sent to his former address and forwarded to Lighthouse, all people who clearly had no idea that he was dying of AIDS; some old-fashioned spectacles; two books, one about the history of the Jews which was an enormous tome and looked like it would have been hard work even for those in the peak of health and the other was an Iris Murdoch novel; plus sundry toiletries, a Walkman and several tapes mostly of Wagner and Mozart. And that was just about it, apart from his clothes which hadn't been worn in all the time he'd been at Lighthouse.

Death was certainly not hidden away on the unit, even to the extent that I heard one visitor complain that she had heard laughter in the day room while her friend was dying. That contradiction, of course, was precisely what many people cherished about London Lighthouse. When I first arrived as a volunteer I wondered how someone like me would know who was in the terminal stages and therefore who should not be disturbed. Was there a sign on the door, I asked Sister Peter, but she just smiled and said, 'Oh no, you just come and go as normal and you might even be asked to go in and be with them.' Wherever possible, no one was left alone to die on the unit, and when I witnessed the death of Ralph I was relieved to see just how easy and natural it all seemed to be.

The body remained in the room for some time so that friends and relatives could slowly say their goodbyes. I took them cups of tea, walking in and out freely and without embarrassment. It was the first time I had seen a dead body so close and although I had felt apprehensive and a little anxious beforehand, when I looked at Ralph (and I made a point of looking as it would have been very easy to put blinkers on) there seemed nothing remarkable or strange about it. In one way he still looked like the Ralph I had seen brought into the unit three weeks earlier, but in another way it was nothing like him. His body had been vacated and the shell that remained said little about the man that I had known apart from being a final reminder of his physical presence.

I saw life and death mingle at Lighthouse in a way that

I had never before experienced. Christopher Spence once recounted the story of a young man who had worked at Lighthouse as caretaker and who had died as a result of an accident: 'One day he was there, as usual, singing his way in and out of every room in the building; the next morning he was dead. Even at London Lighthouse, where we experience so many deaths, this was a shattering event: for many people it was their first brush with sudden, violent death and the whole organisation was stunned.

'A week later, following an inquest, his body was brought back to our own mortuary at Lighthouse where we were planning to hold his funeral. The coffin was brought in through the front door, and set down briefly in our beautiful reception area, with sunlight streaming in through the light well. The coffin was carried by his closest friends at work, and flowers were laid on it. Many people were present, able at last to realise what had happened, and to hold each other and cry. I noticed as this simple, spontaneous, informal ceremony took place that, all around us, it was business as usual. People using services in the building were moving from room to room; members of the public were coming in from the street on their way to lunch in our cafe. At one moment I saw an elderly person, with as far as I know no connection with the young man who had died, pause and join our group, and cry a little with us.

'It seemed clear to me, at that moment, that both processes could proceed side by side; neither one inhibiting the other. London Lighthouse could grieve its loss; and the world about us could go about the business of living. I tried mentally to transfer this scenario into the mainstream world; say the bank next door, or the town hall, with people cashing cheques, or paying their rates, while people in the institution engaged quite openly and unselfconsciously in dealing with their loss. What a gift this might be, and who knows what humanising effects it might have on the way our institutions work?'

While there may have been people who believed that Lighthouse's view of AIDS as a transformative disease, denied the negative and was inhibiting and exclusive because of it, I never heard any criticism of the staff with regards to how they dealt with the actuality and aftermath of death. The practicality with which it was handled, the honesty with which it was talked about and the way in which the bereaved were supported for days, months – years even – after they'd suffered their loss, spoke more than the numerous sheets of paper on which were written London Lighthouse's aims to change engrained social attitudes about death and dying.

There is no doubt that in our society dying people are very often denied the knowledge of what is going on. I had experienced this myself when a man I knew professionally was suddenly taken ill. His friends and colleagues were very concerned because there was some suggestion that it might be cancer. He went into hospital for some tests but three weeks later was back at work with a clean bill of health and everyone breathed a huge sigh of relief. The doctors, he said, had told him that there was nothing suspicious about the lump on his neck, it was completely benign and he had every chance of living to a ripe old age. Nine weeks later, however, this man suddenly died leaving everyone in a state of complete disbelief. Apparently the tumour had been so acute that nothing could be done to alter its destructive course. Sensing that this man might not be able to handle the gloomy prognosis and encouraged by a few close relatives who were the only ones to know the truth, the doctors concocted an elaborate tale and told him a blatant lie which was fed down to all but his nearest and dearest.

It is also true that death is often unnecessarily prolonged in our culture and tranquilisers prescribed which blur the ability of the dying to make final decisions about funerals, possessions and saying goodbyes. Death, dying and bereavement are all taboo subjects with rituals denied and open displays of grief regarded with suspicion and fear. A bereaved person is allotted a certain number of days during which abject despair is considered appropriate but following that they are expected to pull themselves together.

The term private grief is very apposite, meaning that it is permissible to cry in the seclusion of your own home, but not permissible in public. People feel uncomfortable witnessing other people's tears and so the bereaved learn to put grief into a context to make it comfortable for other people. I knew this myself only too well from my own family's experience. At the time of my brother's death there were friends who shrank back unable to handle my grief which they saw as distressing and demanding. Many, who were supportive at the time, later stopped allowing me to talk about it. I could see the shutters come down at the merest hint of the subject. I know my mother felt this even more keenly than me, and when over ten years later I had to interview several bereaved mothers and fathers for an article on the subject, every one of them mentioned the fact that people wouldn't allow them to talk about it. Shortly after my brother's death I discovered a poem written by my mother hidden away in a drawer. It contained these lines:

The storm in the dream and the tears on my cheek
are all tidied away during the day,
folded like my nightdress under the pillow . . .

I thought them beautiful and apt and have remembered them ever since.

Christopher Spence was convinced of the positive effects of crying. In 'A Homecoming and the Harvest. (A Counsellor's View of Death, Dying and Bereavement)' he writes: 'We know that children can recover spontaneously from hurtful experiences through the natural process of emotional release – crying, trembling, yawning, laughing and so on. However, for most of us these responses were thoroughly interfered with very early in our lives by adults who confused the healing process with the hurt itself, and did what they could to stop it. As a result we have tended to internalise to some degree the notion that the release of feelings, especially through crying, is inappropriate and undesirable. So, confronted with someone needing to cry out their grief or shake off their fear, we are likely to intervene to interrupt the emotional release and calm the distressed person down, thus becoming more comfortable ourselves, while leaving them with their feelings of distress intact.'

One of the first members of staff at Lighthouse remembered crying all the time during the early days of working there, though he wonders if that would be acceptable behaviour now. Part of the co-counselling philosophy was that your tears are your grief, to do with your own history and nothing to do with other people. This was a dramatic shift in the way he'd been brought up to internalise his feelings and he described his experience of Lighthouse as 'a rollercoaster of emotion'.

On this subject Geoff Warburton, a former Lighthouse press and public relations officer, once said, 'AIDS touches on every taboo we have in society – death, dying, sexuality, disability, drug use and is loaded with emotion – grief, love, anger and fury. It's just as difficult for a gay man to let out his feelings and cry about it as it is for a heterosexual man. One of the things the gay man internalises is that he's not a 'real man' and one of the things he may do to compensate for that is to try at all costs to be a real man, and being a real man in this country is not to cry.'

London Lighthouse went against the grain, therefore, in permitting, and even encouraging, open and spontaneous displays of grief and to a large extent this openness gave me the opportunity to free myself of inhibition. I was disappointed, however, by my own reaction when one afternoon I found myself talking to Julian about his illness. Julian was one of the people I grew closest to during my time as a volunteer and who taught me a lot about AIDS and the way people handled it.

He had been telling me how before his diagnosis he never cried but now there were a few chosen special people he felt able to cry in front of – namely his partner, the nurse at his local surgery, his dog. He then went on to tell me about a close friend who had recently died in a great deal of pain. Julian was visibly upset as he talked about this and his voice broke as he recounted the final moments of his friend's life, and how on the point of death his friend had been able to gather enough strength to tell Julian that he loved him.

Remembering this distressing and moving scene was too much for Julian, and he broke down in tears, shaking with emotion as he recalled the injustice of the situation. I sat there not really knowing what to do. I wanted to respect his privacy, especially since he had just been telling me how he only liked to be hugged by those he felt closest to, and, as close as I may have felt to Julian at that time, I did not feel our brief friendship put me in a position to reach out to him. Although I would have liked to touch him and take him in my arms, I did not dare. I'm not sure if I did the right thing or not and part of me still feels ineffectual and cowardly at the way I reacted.

The nurses on the unit were trained to communicate and to allow people to talk about their deaths. Grace said she had come to work at Lighthouse because she had always wanted to do palliative care and had been disappointed with the NHS where she found the nurses had a basic lack of knowledge and were afraid to address the issue. 'It's very hard always to be honest with a resident,' she told me. 'If someone asks me, "Am I going to die?" they might be hoping I'll say, "No, not yet" but I have to tell them the truth, so I'll say, "Yes, you may die soon." If I feel someone doesn't want to know the answer I may put the question back to them, "Do you think you're going to die?" because in actual fact they may want it confirmed without realising it. But I don't think all people should be made to face up to their death. If people are in denial, this may be because it is the only place that they feel able to function and cope. Some people think you should bring everyone through to accepting their death (and certainly the people around them will have a better time if that's the case) but it just might not be possible and we have to recognise that fact.'

I found that the residents I met on the unit on the whole spoke frankly about death. Jamie was a good example. He told me how he had recently returned to Leeds to see his parents because he wanted to tell them that he had the money to pay for his funeral and to make plans for it. He felt being terminally ill had put him in a position to negotiate. Although he did not get on with his family, he knew that when he died they would be the ones left to deal with the funeral and so communication was vital: 'I wanted to make it clear that I would try to accommodate their needs but that my ideas and those of my friends also had to be considered. So when I went up there I told them I hadn't yet made a decision but I wanted to discuss it with them. My fear was that my mother, who is an extremely manipulative person, would want to control it all from her own power base and insist on doing it all her own way. Although I tried to discuss my funeral frankly with my parents, they obviously didn't want to have an objective conversation and so in the end nothing was accomplished. I sensed that my mother wasn't allowing me to get at what I'd come to target and so I dropped it.

'A few weeks later I phoned and we had a one and a half hour talk on the subject. Sometimes it's easier to have an objective conversation on the phone because it's neutral territory and body language doesn't get in the way. My mother was very reasonable to start with and said she'd go along with anything I wanted, but when I said I wanted to be cremated in London, she started on about how heartbroken my sister and brother would be if the funeral wasn't held in Leeds. The truth is that I don't actually want my family at my funeral but not to include them and let them go through a state of grieving on their own would be heartless and cruel. I know my mother feels that ever since I was a kid I've been trying to keep her out of my life and now she thinks I'm trying to keep her out of my death, but she doesn't understand that the reason I have to keep my distance is to stop myself from being swamped and taken over by her.'

The telephone conversation had been inconclusive and nothing was decided about where Jamie was to be cremated. He thought it best to wait until nearer the end when, no doubt, he would be forced into a final confrontation. At the same time he realised that by then it might well be too late to make things happen the way he wanted them to.

Much of Father John White's pastoral care at Lighthouse involved work with the recently bereaved as they came to terms with the death of a loved one. This usually included conducting or advising on funerals – an area which often had to be handled with extreme sensitivity, particularly when no previous arrangements had been made. Father John told me it was not uncommon for the family of a deceased person to decide on the sort of funeral they wanted, even when friends might be entirely opposed to it on the grounds that it did not reflect that person's tastes or beliefs. Under these difficult circumstances it was Father John's task somehow to steer a middle course and accommodate everyone's wishes as best he could.

He told me of one recent case where parents, who had been estranged from their son for over fifteen years, had travelled down from Scotland to be with him during the last few days of his life. Unfortunately Paul had died shortly after the reconciliation had taken place and his parents were left feeling bereft and full of remorse. Having had no involvement in their son's life, they were now at great pains to involve themselves in his death and immediately set about arranging his funeral according to their own beliefs and wishes.

His mother, being a staunch Methodist, was certain that her son had kept his faith until the end, even though he had not brought up the subject of religion during the final hours of his life. His friends, on the other hand, resented the family's interference and tried to make them understand that Paul had never been a religious man and that a Methodist service would be wholly inappropriate since it did not reflect Paul's life or beliefs.

With gentle encouragement Father John helped them to

choose a light religious service which was finally acceptable both to Paul's family and to his friends. How much
better it would have been if Paul had made his own
arrangements before he died, but sadly, because he had
never come to terms with his own death, he had not been
able to contemplate the reality of his own funeral. By contrast Jamie was striving to organise an event which would
somehow satisfy both his friends and his family, despite a
virtual breakdown in communication with the latter.

Unfortunately not everyone was as frank and down-to-
earth about their funeral arrangements as Jamie was, even
though to get as far as Lighthouse usually meant a degree
of insight into the disease. I did, however, meet one
woman who had never talked about what was wrong
with her and although she was dying never referred to her
own mortality. The nurses had to respect her wish
although there was a sense of frustration at such manifest
denial. Sometimes relatives were also expected to collude
and perpetuate the lie. It was often left to one of the
counsellors to tell relatives the truth when a member of
their family was dying, but some relatives chose not to
hear it.

One counsellor told me: 'Sometimes if a mother is
talking about a holiday she plans to take her son on, or is
trying to find out when his leave date is, I just say, "Stop!
Listen to what's being said. I know it's very difficult for
you but your son is not going to leave this place." I want
her to know that time is short and that there may be
things she wants to say to her son which she otherwise
might not think to say. But if she says, "No, he's going
to pull through," then I change tacks and go with it.'
Counselling was often like steering into a skid – there was
no point in putting the brakes on and trying to go the
other way when someone was incapable of digesting what

was being said. Also a person might have heard the words but not yet have registered the meaning.

But this reaction was rare on the unit. I was frequently impressed at the matter-of-fact way in which death was dealt with and I found myself able to talk in a remarkably uninhibited manner to people who were dying about immensely delicate subjects. Sometimes people would voice their fears and then it was difficult to know what to say. I realised then that with any other fear it was so easy to brush it aside saying, 'Don't worry, it'll probably never happen.' But when someone has AIDS such sentiments are false, cowardly and unhelpful. When one resident confided in me that it was all the high-tech acute care equipment which put the fear of God in him, I could do nothing else but agree with him. I had been intrigued by the machinery but looking at it from the other side I could see how terrifying all this furniture of death must be.

One resident asked his nurse to stop feeding him because he wanted to die more quickly, but I overheard her telling him that refusing to eat a bowl of Wheetabix wasn't going to make him die any more quickly although it might make him die less comfortably. The more time I'd spent with residents and the longer I'd seen them around – even if I hadn't actually had more than a couple of minutes conversation with them – the harder it obviously was when they died.

And when George reached the terminal stages everyone took it badly. His final visit was his third stay on the unit. This was the first time he'd had a single room and seeing his now wasted body propped up against a great pile of pillows and watching his parents – who had come all the way from Cornwall – care for him with the utmost devotion, was both heartening and humbling. I was not there when he died but arrived twelve hours later to find a clean and empty room. There was something unnerving about the way that just a few hours earlier the room had been filled with all his belongings and mess and now it was as if he had never even occupied the space. George was one of those people who had been popular with everyone, so when he died his death made an impact on the whole building. I overheard a little bit of friction at reception between two volunteers – one of whom had known him intimately. She was anxious in case his clinitron bed, which was in the process of being carried through reception, should be seen by his parents who might be unnecessarily upset. She wanted to have the bed taken through the side entrance, whereas the other volunteer could not see what the fuss was about – 'For goodness sake,' I heard him say in an exasperated tone of voice, 'it's only a bed.'

Some of those who were still quite well also spoke openly of their approaching death. I met one very fretful man in his eartly forties who constantly bemoaned the fact that his friends weren't doing enough for him. He said his main worry was that he might die before he'd found a good home for his pets. He had a cat and a dog and up until a week previously he had had a goldfish as well. 'I know it sounds awful,' he confessed, 'but I'm glad it died because who on earth would have wanted to look after a goldfish?'

One evening I listened to two men talking about how they coped with the knowledge that their death was fairly imminent. One of them, who had recently had several painful operations for abscesses in his anus and who couldn't walk without a great deal of discomfort, had twice fought his way back from the edge of death. Both men agreed that they no longer made plans so that if someone said, 'Let's meet next week,' they would say

'Let's wait and see what happens on the day.' They were both celibate, although one of them confessed that he still shopped around just to see what was available. Like so many people I met who had AIDS he felt it was in everyone's interest to make something commonplace out of the disease and he told me that the only way he coped was by 'taking the piss out of it'.

If you are not HIV positive, all the therapeutic empathy in the world won't tell you what it feels like to lose most of your friends. But, to get a glimpse of what multiple grief means, one counsellor at Lighthouse suggested thinking of the following people – namely your partner, your best friend, a good friend, someone that you once had a sexual relationship with, someone you've known from a very early age, and an old friend you haven't seen for years. Now put them together in the same room, and imagine that they're all dead. That's what it feels like for many people affected by HIV and AIDS, some of whom have witnessed the decimation of their entire community.

AIDS is different from any other terminal illness in this respect. It wipes out whole communities with those affected, like the inhabitants of a concentration camp, forced into the inescapable position of waiting for something awful to happen, while those left standing suffer from the same feelings of guilt and bewilderment as the survivors of the holocaust had done. Although HIV-negative people might have been thought of as the lucky ones, they often felt desperate and alone, wishing rather to be in the same position as their dead friends because then at least they would no longer feel this way. A typical response was 'I don't want to make any new friends with gay men because they'll only get AIDS and die.' I also knew that some funerals at Lighthouse were poorly attended due to battle fatigue. Multiple deaths meant multiple funerals and it was hardly surprising that people sometimes reached a point where they simply couldn't face going through one more death.

When I was working on the unit I met one man who dreaded coming into the building because he was now visiting his fifth sick friend. I could see that he was at breaking point. He had nursed three of these friends and couldn't face the idea of nursing a fourth. The friend he'd come to see, like him, was an actor and was recovering from PCP. Both were fit, youthful, attractive men, and it struck me then, more acutely than ever before, what a cruel disease this was to strike such young people, many of whom were extremely image conscious. 'You see,' he said, 'it still hasn't sunk in that this is happening to me. When I looked through my address book the other day I realised that about three-quarters of the people in it were dead. I couldn't possibly cross them all off, it would have been like starting the count down to my own death, so instead I've put the book in a drawer and memorised the few telephone numbers I still need.'

Coping with loss takes time and people generally need months before they are able to carry on with normal life again. But a person mourning the loss of someone with AIDS often had to deal with another bereavement within a few weeks, and subsequently another, and another. So there was no opportunity for recovery. Someone dealing with multiple deaths would eventually move from the victim to the survivor role, though a very small proportion developed symptoms of paranoia, believing themselves to be surrounded by evil, either self-inflicted or instigated by some supernatural force.

Working with people with AIDS takes its toll, particularly in a place like Lighthouse where personal involvement and intimacy were seen as an important componant in fighting the stigma and isolation surrounding HIV. For some people, it had at times all been too much and the desire to retreat was never far away. One manager – whose position meant that she was not even working on the frontline – told me she could easily name thirty people she had known reasonably well who had died of AIDS in the last eighteen months. 'Sometimes in the past I've tried to prepare myself by holding back,' she said, 'but one friend who was dying noticed this and said to me, "I know you're holding back but I'm not going to have it because I need friends." I was very grateful to him for saying that because we got very close after that and I learnt a lot from him. I was with him when he died which was hard but also very important.'

Suzi had been working at Lighthouse for three months before she became aware that she had contained but not controlled her feelings of loss. After work when she was out drinking with her friends, she would listen to them talking about what had happened during their working day, but she felt unable to contribute because it would have been unacceptable to talk about death. Then, one day, she was standing in reception watching the under-takers carry a coffin from the building when a volunteer asked her who was being taken away. When he discovered that it was a man he had been good friends with, he told her that he was going to stand on the corner of the street and wave his friend goodbye. It was this simple, final act of friendship which made Suzi break down and cry, enabling her at last to release all the sadness that she had so far managed to keep a lid on.

Working with the dying had affected the way the Head of Counselling led his life: 'I use death as a yardstick for a lot of things, not least to look at how I'm living my life,' Khaldun said. 'When I'm not living my life the way I should then I start fearing death and I'm full of regret. I look at what's gone wrong and I realise my values have gone a bit off the rails. A year ago I started re-evaluating my friendships by thinking about who I would want to have sitting with me when I died: it made me realise what I wanted from my friendships and which friends I felt closest to.' There were also a few members of staff and volunteers who could not cope with death. These were people who often found it difficult to form relationships and generally didn't stay long at Lighthouse.

Equally it was possible to get too involved, which was particularly damaging if you began to resent that involvement or if it clouded your professional judgement. But I knew many members of staff and volunteers who got extremely involved with service users and whose work was not in any way impaired. I realised that initially I too had considered holding back in my relationships with people who had AIDS. I wanted to get close and yet was frightened of getting too close. I soon discovered however that friendships at Lighthouse were organic and spontaneous, and could not be limited by such a timid notion of detachment. Once I had overcome this fear, I wanted these relationships to be as good as they could possibly be, because for the first time in my life I didn't feel I could let things go ahead at the leisurely pace they normally did.

For people who had the virus, however, it was different and a certain amount of distancing was often necessary. One man I met on the unit, who had been a resident several times, said that each time he'd come he'd made friends with someone who had later died, so this time he was determined to keep himself to himself and not make a new friend even if it meant being antisocial. A man who worked in the information office, and who had been involved in Lighthouse from its earliest days, told me how he used to be a home support volunteer. 'Although I'd been diagnosed HIV for some time, I was less connected with my own status then and didn't know people who were sick or dying, but there came a point when the intense involvement was too much for me and I couldn't bear to watch another person die.'

He told me that he'd had the test in 1985 in order to set his mind at rest, since he'd never indulged in unsafe practices and his doctor was confident that this was an American disease which was unlikely to affect many British men. But his doctor was wrong and, instead of the negative result he'd anticipated, he was told he had the virus and would probably be dead within two years.

'At first people like me who were diagnosed around that time felt complete despair but then the mood changed and there was a lot of very hopeful, almost evangelical, talk and we began to think that if we did enough work on each other we could carry on indefinitely. We saw each other living longer and longer and the prognosis was no longer two years but ten.' For this man, however, things took a downward turn at the beginning of 1990 when three people he knew well died within three weeks of each other. It was at this point that he gave up his work as a home support volunteer to concentrate instead on providing an information service for people with HIV.

He, like many others I met, regretted having had the test. People who were living quite healthy lives with HIV often compared it to living with a timebomb because you knew that at some point it had to explode but you had no idea when or where. As one person put it: 'Everything has changed but nothing has changed. I know I have HIV but I don't realise it.'

Philip Sanderson also said that given the choice he would never have had the test. 'I think it's a useless piece of information,' he said. 'As soon as you label yourself with HIV it becomes self-limiting. Depending on how strong your character is, many people – no matter how much counselling they get – become very self-destructive and die very quickly because stress automatically reduces the immune system.' He thought that people who suddenly found themselves in hospital with PCP or toxiplasmosis were infinitely better off because then at least they knew what they were working with and fighting against, whereas with HIV the foe was hidden and there was nothing to grasp hold of. It was an amorphous and lurking enemy which insidiously wormed its way first into people's psyche and then eventually into their physical being.

Philip Sanderson was one of the few members of staff at Lighthouse who didn't seem to mind sticking his neck out. He had opinions and wasn't afraid of voicing them, even if they weren't always what people wanted to hear. He was totally committed to his work at Lighthouse and passionate about getting it right. Although at first I thought him rather gruff and uncommunicative, I later found him to be a disarmingly honest man of great integrity.

He came from the north east of England from a working-class background and had worked in London for six years, periodically going back to attend professional courses in the north. It was during a course specialising in neuromedical and neurosurgical nursing that he found out something which changed his life.

'It was 1985 and I was twenty-three years old. After having a wild fling, I decided to be sensible and go to the local 'clap' clinic for a check up where bloods were taken and sensitive areas of my body swabbed and scraped. "Does this happen to everyone?" I remember thinking. I had no fear of the unexpected. After all penicillin cured all didn't it? I went home and carried on with life as if nothing had happened. Going back the following week I wondered, "God I hope I haven't got syphilis. Those bloody penicillin injections hurt like hell." I walked into the clinic and took a seat. The atmosphere seemed tense. The nurses crowding around their office door were looking at me and I smiled back, a little embarrassed but all the same chuffed. "If only they knew I was gay," I thought to myself. Minutes later a huge and officious-looking man peered out of a small consulting room and shouted my number. I walked in, sat down in a relaxed pose and smiled.'

Sanderson was then given his result without any attempt at softening the blow. The consultant avoided eye-contact by staring straight ahead into space. He told Sanderson that he had AIDS (which in fact was the wrong diagnosis since he was still only HIV positive) and that he didn't have long to live. As a final reproach the consultant said, 'You have been very stupid, haven't you? As a nurse you should have known better.'

He was then weighed and told to return in two weeks time, which he never did. Instead he spent the next few months fighting the directors of nursing and senior tutors on his course all of whom wanted to get rid of him because they feared infection. In the end they didn't succeed and he went on to pass his exams with high grades.

'I then put AIDS behind me,' he said. 'No one other than the school tutors and their colleagues knew, no friends, no family. After all, I am a Geordie. Would anyone tolerate or accept me? My family loved me – I knew they would, but the media is very powerful and their message was "NO".'

When Sanderson saw the advertisement in *Nursing Times* for the position of charge nurse at London Lighthouse he applied, not because of his connection with HIV and AIDS but purely because it was a good career move. After starting in the job and during the induction course, for some reason unknown to him he broke down in tears and told all the people in the room that he was HIV positive. 'This was the first time that I had discussed or mentioned HIV for four years. I was home, I was safe, I felt respected.'

· *Thirteen* ·

Feeling at home, safe and respected were all feelings I had had about Lighthouse. Respect may have been in short supply at the time that the *Independent* published my article but by standing my ground and refusing to retreat from the fray, I was soon able to retrieve it.

The response to that article was a turning point in my relationship with Lighthouse. Although at the time it caused me much misery and for a while made me bitterly regret ever having put pen to paper, I eventually came to regard the incident as an immensely valuable experience, not least because it gave me access to two people's lives whose friendship I subsequently came to treasure. Julian was one of them.

I first met Julian when I was working on reception and true to form he joked about his illness. He had just heard how a woman employed by Lighthouse had been knocked down by a bus but had discharged herself from hospital on account of having to look after her eight children. Hearing this, Julian said: 'Having children is obviously an incentive to live, I should get hold of some.'

I got to know him because of his strong feelings about my article and I got to like him because of the generosity he showed me in subsequently coming to my support. He was someone who was liked and admired by everyone at Lighthouse – not only because of his devilish sense of humour but also because of what a colleague once described as 'his magnificent manner of life.' His one act of defiance, as far as Lighthouse was concerned, was to insist on wearing his identity badge on his crotch despite complaints from a female member of staff. When she challenged him on the matter, telling him that she found it offensive, he retaliated by telling her he found it offensive that she chose to wear her badge on her nipple. He was an immensely resilient man whom I never once heard complain. There was probably a certain amount of denial going on as he admitted to me once that he would never allow himself to think about what lay ahead.

He told me it had all started in 1988 when he began to get severe headaches. 'It never occured to me that I might be HIV positive because I'd had protected sex for at least ten years. These headaches got so bad that eventually the people I was working with packed me off to the company doctor who arranged for some tests, including the HIV test. From then on I don't remember what happened to me – it's all hearsay. My brain just shut down, partly because of the illness but also because I didn't want to know what was going on. Someone – I don't remember who – came with me to get my test results and I can't even remember what my reaction was. Then I started doing silly things at work and was sent in a state of stupor to a private venerologist who immediately admitted me to hospital. Here I was diagnosed as having encephalitis. I'm told I was very bad tempered and just watched television all day long while munching chocolates. I even stomped down the ward once when the Salvation Army were playing outside and screamed at the top of my voice for them to stop.

'In the spring of 1989 the consultant told my partner that I would probably die so they arranged for me to be taken to London Lighthouse, but much to everyone's surprise after about a month I started to come round. I was taking massive doses of AZT and was supported by some incredible friends – including a couple of people from work who came in nearly every day to see how I was: they would cut my nails and tell me off if I hadn't washed.

'Once I was thinking straight again I still had a lot of problems to overcome. I had to relearn how to walk and climb up stairs. I wasn't supposed to leave the building, but I'd often try to wander off on my own. The nurses would put a note in my pocket saying "If Found Please Return to London Lighthouse". The support I got from the nurses was phenomenal and Sheila, a volunteer, took me under her wing. She took me out on bus rides and for trips in her car. All the nurses loved me and I'd call them by any name that came into my head because I could never remember what they were really called. I had great fun. If I couldn't sleep I'd get up at three in the morning and have a drink and a laugh with them. I think just about everyone at Lighthouse was both shocked and delighted that I made such an unexpected mental and physical recovery.

'It was like slowly coming back to life and I felt great because I had no realisation that I had HIV – largely I think because I had no memory of being told. It was only two years later that the truth about this illness really hit me. I had been mooching along for some time with very little wrong with me, when all of a sudden my stomach started playing up and I lost two and a half stone in weight in the space of four months.

'In the initial days at Lighthouse people were mostly

dying and I was someone who had been brought in for terminal care but who had somehow miraculously got up and gone home again. My confidence had been boosted by having made what everyone called a remarkable recovery, so when I lost all this weight it was a great blow and I began to worry. Then one day I came home from the doctor and looked at a letter he'd given me; on it was clearly stated that I now had an AIDS diagnosis. He'd probably told me but like so many other things I'd managed to block it out.

'It was a great shock – far, far worse than being told I was HIV positive. I rang up everyone I knew who I thought might be able to help. I asked my partner to meet me for lunch but when we met he seemed very unconcerned and just said that he knew already. He wasn't dismissive but he just didn't know what to say to me. So that afternoon I rang up my home support volunteer who I get on exceptionally well with and he just listened, which is all I really wanted. When my partner came home that evening, I insisted we talk about it because I wanted us both to acknowledge that I was not HIV positive anymore but had a terminal illness which I intended to fight all the way.'

Julian was full of appreciation for his friends and for his family. Since his diagnosis he had been shown nothing but love and kindness, and he treasured the deeper relationships he had formed since the onset of his illness. He spoke with great affection of his partner, who in his eyes had been 'bloody brilliant' but who he felt needed as much support as he did because partners couldn't fight AIDS whereas people with AIDS could. London Lighthouse meant a lot to Julian and he always felt very protected within its four walls. In 1989 he had a poem printed in *Lighthouse News* which he introduced like this:

I wrote this poem after leaving the London Lighthouse
residential unit almost fully recovered. I now work as a
volunteer on the reception desk, and if you are passing
please pop in and say hi! You will be made more than
welcome by me and all the staff at Lighthouse. We
need your support and, in return, you will receive love,
understanding and great strength from us:

I am Gay
I am homosexual
I have AIDS

I am at one with my God
I am at one with
my brothers

My friends are still friends
My family supportive and loving
My lover is wonderful
I love him
I love life
I love my dog
I am what I am
I pray more
I cry more
I cry while I write this
I laugh more
I love more
I live more
I am whole
I am myself
I will not change
I will survive

I WILL SURVIVE

In a talk Christopher Spence gave at St Marylebone Centre for Healing and Counselling in early 1990, he said of Julian: 'We were told he had severe dementia, that he was an extremely angry, disconnected and difficult patient, and that his prognosis was extremely poor.

'In the very many weeks that he was with us, with an enormous amount of time and support from people who work at London Lighthouse – all of whom would agree that the work with Julian was very hard at times – he engaged, perhaps for the first time in his life, in the struggle to find and connect with himself, to face and come to terms with his diagnosis, and to resolve his life honestly.'

Julian said that he had become more sensitive in every way since his illness – sensitive to music and moods, to nuances in language, to the look in a person's eye, the sincerity of a smile. After he told me this, for a while I felt very self-conscious in his presence, imagining his finely tuned perceptions would immediately detect any insincerity or exaggeration on my part.

Nine months after I first met Julian, he had deteriorated markedly. He was no longer quite the 'appetising little man' he had once been described to me as, although his sprightly elfin demeanour never failed to be attractive. Like so many people with AIDS, he was taking numerous drugs. His kitchen was more like a chemist's counter than a place to prepare food. He had a special container for all his drugs and an alarm would sound to remind him when to take the next dose. He once listed his medication to me and it made a daunting daily cocktail: 300 mils of AZT; Septrin – the prophylaxis for PCP; Ketoconazole – the prophylaxis for candida; Albendazole for his parasitic stomach infection; Immodium for diarrhoea; Acyclovir for herpes; as well as Buscopan and Codeine Phosphate for whenever his gut played up.

Despite so much being wrong, Julian never seemed to lose heart, no matter how bad the news was. On one occasion when we met in the cafe he told me casually that he had lost a lot of weight because he was now only able to absorb 2 per cent of his food. Another time he told me he had found signs of KS on his legs. But Julian's stamina was phenomenal – somehow he always seemed to bounce back and as with other people at Lighthouse, who had a similarly pugnacious attitude towards their illness, I somehow never felt he was going to die.

But sadly I never saw Julian alive again after the Christmas of 1991. I was at Lighthouse on the day that the news of his death came through and witnessed the impact it made on the whole organisation. There was shock, sadness and a great many tears. It was a Friday morning and the weekly open day was about to begin in the Ian McKellen hall with roughly sixty people attending. Before the slide show got under way Christopher Spence stood up and told the assembled gathering about Julian explaining why a memorial candle was burning in his memory and why the staff and volunteers taking part might appear distracted or upset.

London Lighthouse experienced many deaths, year in, year out, but Julian's death was different because it affected everybody. I don't think I met any service user more popular. He was an unusually generous man in his open and accepting attitude towards others and although he had strong opinions, he was never dogmatic or censorious. At his funeral Christopher Spence described him as 'generous, brave and feisty' and one of his oldest friends said that 'though small in stature, he was a big man and a big friend'. The Ian McKellen hall was packed with those who knew him well, as well as those who barely knew him at all, but all of whom had in some way been touched by his courageous spirit.

I had not cried on first hearing of Julian's death which surprised me as he was one of the people at Lighthouse whom I cared for most. But witnessing other people's grief somehow seemed to inhibit my own. I felt that it was a matter of taking my place in line and at first my feelings took second place to the very considerable grief felt by the organisation as a whole. I had never experienced this kind of collective grief before and such a public display of sadness made Julian's death suddenly seem less private and less personal.

Funerals can be very useful and necessary things for they allow you to grieve. In my experience, when people you don't know very well die, it is easy to have a quick gush of sadness and then get on with your life as before. With Julian even that gush was repressed because I was surrounded by people who I felt had more right to grieve than I had. The funeral, however, sorted out all these mixed emotions and my sadness suddenly broke through the barriers which I had unconsciously erected.

It was an intensely touching occasion with his family sitting on one side of the hall and his partner and close friends on the other: we listened to his favourite music being played and heard him talked about in loving and admiring terms. It is easy to adulate the dead, especially during a funeral service, but Julian was undoubtedly an exceptional man. I felt privileged to have known him, regretting only that our friendship had never developed further. The funeral was made even sadder for me as I looked around the room and saw Sam, Liam and Richard. For them no doubt Julian's funeral was a time for painful reflection.

Julian was greatly missed at Lighthouse. One elderly man who used the drop-in area much like a social club commented that Thursdays were never the same after that and that even six months later he still expected to see Julian walk through the door greeting everyone in his usual snappy, sanguine manner.

In the eighteen months I spent at London Lighthouse I got to know just a handful of people well. Like all my relationships at Lighthouse, these were goldfish-bowl relationships in that they were extraneous to my life outside. This wasn't because I wished to separate my two worlds but because the nature of these new friendships worked best on a one-to-one basis and had nothing to do with socialising in the conventional sense of the word. HIV and AIDS set the course and marked the boundaries while Lighthouse provided the setting.

Sam was the man who made HIV and AIDS real for me. In the three months before I came to know him, my involvement with Lighthouse was comparatively super-ficial. I was inspired by the philosophy and by some people's remarkably resilient spirit but I felt as if I was on the edge always looking on, never really able to be at the centre of things. When people died I felt their loss in terms of an absence but it was not a private loss. In a very personal sense, Sam became for me the human face of Lighthouse.

It was an unusual friendship in so much as compared with my other friends, Sam and I had very little in common. But despite our differences there was an under-lying bond which had been apparent almost from the day we first met.

Sam had previously worked for the family import and export antiques firm which he had run for twenty years. And although he had established a highly successful and reputable business, in 1987 he had decided to sell up since so many years of devoted service had left him exhausted and badly in need of a change. He relished the idea of doing something totally different with his life and was looking forward to a new and exciting challenge. Tragically, the challenge he had to face was not the change of career he had so eagerly anticipated but instead the challenge of HIV and the imminent threat of AIDS which took a grip of his life at about the time the sale of the business was completed.

Sam had always mixed with a group of gay men who he described to me as 'extremely proper' – many of whom worked in the City and none of whom identified with the gay scene either politically or emotionally. Sam was obviously nothing like them but was accepted in their circle since his partner of twenty-five years standing was the centre-piece of the group. He told me he had led a remarkably sheltered existence in this respect and that even as late as 1986 AIDS had not registered with him as anything that could affect his life. It was not a subject talked about by men whose only reference to the 'gay plague' was to acknowledge a new law which said: 'Thou shalt not sleep with an American.'

Since Sam had an aversion to newspapers and had never been introduced to the gay press his knowledge of safe sex was minimal. Until 1985 this, however, was an irrelevance since in the late seventies he had been infected by the Hepatitis B virus and as a result had opted for a life of celibacy. The decision did not affect his partner since they lived separately and had maintained a purely platonic relationship for most of the twenty years they had been together. 'We were lovers without the sex,' Sam explained.

'Hepatitis B was like a rehearsal for what was to come next,' he once told me, 'because it is far, far more contagious than HIV and the virus practically jumps out at you. Once, when I was cooking dinner for some friends, I cut my finger and was so paranoid about infecting my guests that I took them all out to a restaurant instead.'

When in January 1986 the hospital told Sam that much to their surprise the Hepatitis B virus had cleared, it appeared to be splendid news. It was indeed rare for this to happen after so many years of infection and had the virus persisted it could well have resulted in cirrhosis or even cancer of the liver. But for Sam the timing was unfortunate since he was still unaware of the dangers of HIV. 'When I was told I was clear,' he said, 'I asked my doctor if this meant that I could now behave like a butterfly, and I remember him saying something about there still being other things around. I understood what he was getting at as I'd heard of AIDS but I was still incredibly ignorant about the risks.'

He always maintained that had the first Government advertising campaign, which spread the message 'Don't Die of Ignorance' through the images of icebergs and volcanoes, appeared six months earlier he would have realised the dangers in time and consequently would have managed to avoid infection. The advertisements shocked him into submission and he ceased to have unsafe sex from that moment on.

Unfortunately, a few months later and after only a handful of short-lived sexual encounters, Sam became infected with the HIV virus. He was never sure who gave it to him but he knew it could only have been one of three people. But at the time of taking the test in 1988, with so little recent sexual experience, he was confident that the result would be negative and only decided to go ahead with the test at his doctor's suggestion.

'I'd been celibate for so many years and since being cleared had had so few partners that I really wasn't expecting a positive result. I wasn't nervous about the result until the day of the appointment and then suddenly a slight panic crept over me and I began to wonder if there was a possibility that I might be positive after all. When I went into the surgery, my doctor was looking down at the piece of paper in front of him and immediately started telling me the results of some liver function tests that I'd had done, knowing full well that the only result I was really interested in was that of my HIV test. It was an ominous sign and I knew instantly what it meant. Finally he looked up at me and said with great difficulty, "I'm afraid, however, that as far as the HIV test is concerned, you're positive."

'Talk about the world crashing around you. My ears became totally like cotton wool and I remember him muttering something about being able to live well with HIV, but I wasn't able to take a thing in. I was totally stunned, as though I'd been hit on the head by an enormous truncheon. By the time I got home it was 6.30 in the evening. I don't remember crying, though my eyes may have watered a bit, and I was probably whimpering slightly and cursing myself for having been so stupid. Then I took my shoes off and without having anything to eat I lay down on the bed and crashed into a deep and untroubled sleep. I slept soundly like a baby until the next morning. The following day I went to Marks & Spencer and bought five pairs of pyjamas, because although I was totally asymptomatic, I wanted to prepare myself for what lay ahead, rather as a pregnant woman packs her bag before going into hospital to have her baby.'

Sam's first thought was that he wanted to tell every-one he knew that he was HIV positive because he was convinced he only had a few months to live. Instinct, however, told him that it would be folly to broadcast such devastating news and that the only safe course of action was to tell no one, not even his partner of whom he had always felt very protective. His partner, in fact, died two years later following a car accident without ever knowing Sam's status.

After the diagnosis there followed two months of hell. The diagnosis coincided with the sale of the business and instead of his usual twelve-hour day he was working round the clock seven days a week. He was exhausted and rapid weight loss left him looking pale and wan. Colleagues luckily put this down to the strain of having to wind up the family business, which was a useful cover-up for the turmoil of emotions ransacking his mind.

'My diagnosis didn't stop me from being able to work,' he told me. 'Although the horror of it never left me and strangely enough I could still concentrate on the task ahead in a professional sense. Maybe that was because I had the feeling that I was putting my house in order. In a way the strain of overworking helped me get through those nightmarish few weeks.

'Several weeks later when the business was completed and I had time to think straight again, I woke up one night and wrote to my doctor. I've since destroyed the letter but in it I wrote exactly how I felt: what emerged was a great deal of shame. Also I felt angry – but only with myself, not with anyone else. There were certain things I couldn't bare the thought of facing, for instance I hoped and prayed that my father would die before I did so that he'd never have to know about my illness. I tried to end the letter positively and I remember saying something about looking on the bright side, but I didn't really believe that there was a bright side.'

With the business wound up and enough money in the bank to give him a modest private income for at least ten years, Sam found himself feeling alone and lost in his small West London flat. None of his friends knew of his diagnosis and he felt increasingly removed from his partner. All he had room for in his life was the fact that he was terminally ill. At this point he was still convinced that HIV led to imminent and certain death and so embarking on any new projects seemed senseless.

But because of his ignorance of AIDS, Sam felt a need to educate himself and finally enrolled on a Body Positive weekend which he said had an enormous impact on his life, making all the subsequent training courses seem like 'playing with little trains'. 'It was a landmark for me because it allowed me to set foot in the world to which I now belonged whether I liked it or not. It meant that at last I'd admitted to myself that I was HIV positive. Although others on this course tended to vent their anger through violence and screaming, I didn't. I just felt desperately sad.'

Although Sam was pleased to have at last met other people with HIV, he still felt that people with AIDS were an unknown species to him and he told me how once, late at night, he had made his way to the AIDS ward at St Stephen's Hospital, which was pulled down a few months later, because he wanted to see what people with AIDS actually looked like. 'As I tried to find the ward I heard myself whimpering a little and saying to myself, "so this is where these poor sods come to die." I wanted to have a peep at the world to which I might soon belong and gain an insight into my future. But I never found the ward and eventually I left none the wiser.'

It wasn't until Sam came to London Lighthouse that people with AIDS became a familiar sight to him and ceased to be objects of fear and of curiosity. Sam ended up as a volunteer at Lighthouse more by accident than intention. His doctor had told him about the organisation and Sam liked the name because it conjured up pleasant memories of a hotel where he had once stayed in Key West called Lighthouse.

In his mind Sam had imagined that London Lighthouse would be a large converted terrace house in Notting Hill, so he was astonished on seeing its post-modernist exterior and inside its grand white-walled lobby rising to the glass roof two floors above. It reminded him more of a modern art gallery than a residential and day-care centre and, for someone who had always been impressed by packaging, he immediately liked what he saw. He ended up as one of Lighthouse's mainstay volunteers and was immensely popular although when he first arrived he was convinced he was no good at dealing with people.

It was absurd to think of Sam as being no good with people, though I'm sure it was true that before he came to Lighthouse he had had little opportunity to put his con-siderable skills into practice. In fact he very quickly became one of those rare people whom everyone loved and in whom I suspect a great many people confided. I certainly confided in him and it touches me to know that in the course of our friendship he confided more in me than he was accustomed to doing.

When I asked Sam if he was glad to know his HIV status he told me that his feelings on this varied daily depending on the mood he was in, but ultimately, margin-ally, he would have preferred not to have been tested. Why, I wondered? 'Because it has changed my life so radically and because I feel I'm just treading water now,' he said. 'I'm sure if I didn't know I was positive I'd be involved in some new business – I'd probably send a cheque off to Crusaid every now and then, but other than that AIDS wouldn't feature in my life. On the other hand I recognise that there have been great advantages. I'm taking much better care of myself now, I'm much more aware and more approachable. I had no time for people before.'

He also told me that working at Lighthouse had prepared him for the death of his partner. By prepared, he certainly did not mean it had made it any easier, but it had shown him how to help someone die peacefully, comfortably and with dignity. Although his partner did not die of AIDS, it was because of Sam's HIV status and the fact that his life now revolved around the world of AIDS, that gave him the knowledge and courage to help his partner die in the peace and familiarity of his own home.

'I am thankful for what I have learned from HIV,' he told me, 'because it permitted me to love tenderly, to the final closing of his eyes, the man I had loved passionately and faithfully for over twenty-five years. Since then it is not just the fact that I am HIV that has made me into a more approachable sort of person but also because I have experienced bereavement so intimately.'

For someone who was so loquacious, Sam was an intensely private man. He was also honest, self-assured and humorous, without being at all self-analytical or introspective. Though in some ways his outlook on his own prognosis was pretty bleak, and he admitted to me many times that AIDS was a terrible affliction which left people desperately debilitated and disfigured, he did not possess an ounce of self-pity or bitterness. He carried with him, however, a great deal of sadness. 'I'm a bit of a fatalist,' he said, 'I brought this thing upon myself and I've got to deal with it alone.' You had to know Sam well to sense this sadness which he said was ever present whether something good, bad or indifferent happened to him. But to those who only saw him occasionally, as he swept through the drop-in area or bolted down a late lunch in the cafe, it was impossible to detect. He admitted to me that part of his cheerful and breezy manner was a front which, though Lighthouse did not exactly demand of him, they certainly welcomed. 'The show,' he told me, 'is that life's all right. Look at me I've got HIV, but I look OK and I'm still smiling.'

I first met Sam shortly after the unexpected death of his partner when he was still reeling from the shock. The few people outside Lighthouse who knew about his status, he regretted having told. The first person to know had been an ex-colleague of his late partner. Because this woman had apparently acted with breathtaking insensitivity at the time of his partner's death, Sam had lost his temper with her and in a fit of pique inadvertently blurted out: 'What do you know about life and death? I'm HIV positive so I know much more than you will ever know.' He instantly regretted having disclosed such an intimacy to someone he did not care for and was not surprised when from that day on she made no attempt to see or contact him again. He was not sure whether this was because she couldn't handle being in such close proximity to someone who had HIV or because she felt uneasy about having provoked Sam into revealing an innermost secret against his will.

He also told one other person – a gay man who had been a close friend for many years – but the friendship immediately disintegrated on disclosure of this fact. Later, it was tentatively renewed although this time on a very different footing. They now spoke infrequently, AIDS was never discussed and the old intimacy they had previously shared had vanished. It seemed sad and extraordinary to me that one gay man could act so insensitively towards another when both might so easily have been facing the same predicament. But I was to hear this story repeated over and over again. It was, I came to realise, a typical reaction to AIDS resulting from fear and denial. Some people clearly thought that if they never mentioned AIDS, avoided everything written about it, and abandoned all their friends who had it – then somehow it would never touch them.

Although Sam was – to use his own terminology – never promiscuous, the irony was that he had been more sexually active during the past three years than he had been during the previous twenty. The year following diagnosis, however, had left him feeling 'cold and frigid' with no sexual appetite whatsoever. The Hepatitis B virus meant that his world had been turned upside side so that the years of celibacy preceded his diagnosis and prepared him for feeling like a leper. He never told his sexual partners about his status but was adamant on always having safer sex, even if this sometimes brought proceedings to an abrupt and untimely end.

My friendship with Sam was the thing I came to treasure most about my time at Lighthouse. It was special and heartfelt, though I suspect more for me than for him – simply because the feelings that a heterosexual woman has for a gay man have to be more multifarious than the feelings a gay man has for a heterosexual woman. I certainly cared greatly for him, more than for anyone else I met at Lighthouse, and at times the relationship felt quite intense, though in actual fact it wasn't at all – it was warm, lighthearted and relaxed. I think the intensity came from the fact that AIDS hung over us like a dark cloud and created a sense of urgency as well as the fear of losing something special which I had only just found.

· *Fourteen* ·

No matter how much emphasis London Lighthouse put on living well with AIDS, I couldn't fail to notice just how many people had died in the course of a single year. There were thankfully still people like Liam and Sam who were perfectly well and others, like Richard, who had only minor signs of HIV infection, but by far the greatest number had died.

Jamie was one of the few who had initially been extremely ill on the residential unit but twelve months later he seemed to have stabililised. He was under no illusion, however, that he had been given a reprieve and I noticed that as time went by he became more and more agitated. His cabin fever had worsened and he kept admonishing himself for not getting out and about more, for not making the most of his life in London and for not pursuing old friendships or making new ones. Although I encouraged him to join a support group or see a counsellor, he had learned to distrust professionals so thoroughly that he dismissed my suggestions as being inappropriate while at the same time recognising that he badly needed to take some sort of initiative.

He felt depressed, listless and at times, he said, even deranged. He talked of finding himself going down long, dark labyrinths of fantasy which, in their ability to distract him from the real world, were strangely addictive. By indulging in these fantasies he knew that he was only allowing himself to sink further into the quagmire in which he was now submerged. 'It's a terrible vicious circle,' he told me. 'People reject you because they can't really take AIDS on board, and as a result you in turn reject them which of course only perpetuates your isolation and fuels your desperation. The trouble is I'm too much of an outsider. I'm a very self-contained sort of person but it's not a good way to be. I'm too critical of people and too easily disappointed. At the moment I'm licking my wounds after having been very let down by a particular person but eventually I know I'll get sick of sitting indoors all day and I'll charge out again. I sense a resignation in myself. I float along the street looking at a hundred shoe shops and am unable to make a decision about anything in my life.'

He was worried that he had become totally insensate. 'Things just don't seem to touch me any more,' he said. But he was also aware that he was lonely and consequently in a highly vulnerable state. 'If someone reached out a hand to me now, I'd probably grab at it and they wouldn't be able to shake me off. But what sort of way is that to be? It's like clinging to wreckage.'

What Jamie was looking for was someone to share his life with – not necessarily in the physical or sexual sense – but someone who would be there just for him. When he chastised himself for being ineffectual or for complaining too much, I told him that he was being unnecessarily hard on himself. Life had not been easy since his return to England. He had no family or partner to support him and many of his closest friends lived on the other side of the world. In addition to this he found no comfort in a place like Lighthouse which he saw as being accessible only to people who were prepared to play the system.

I had seen and met so many different people at Lighthouse, some of whom were suffering in a similar way to Jamie, that I was convinced if he could only be persuaded to go there he would soon meet some like-minded people. People who would accept him for what he was and who wouldn't think of him as an oddball; who could say to him, 'Yes, I've been there, I know exactly how it feels.' I knew those people existed but Jamie was stubborn and I was reluctant to do more than give him a gentle push.

Like with so many of the people I met who had AIDS, there were times when I was at a complete loss at what to say to Jamie. We would have long telephone conversations during which I knew that nothing I said would begin to soothe his troubled mind. There were no simple solutions or pat answers. I could only listen and acknowledge the fact that I admired him for his strength, for his remarkable lack of self-pity and for his extraordinary ability to keep searching for answers despite being stripped of resources. Of course he did not feel he was any of these things, but Jamie's isolation – partly self-inflicted, partly circumstantial – made his struggle seem all the more real and arduous to me and I knew that had I been in his position, cooped up in a box-like flat in a dingy part of West London with few friends and no family to support me, I should have given up long ago.

I kept in regular contact with Jamie so I usually knew how his life was progressing, but with others, whom I didn't see for months on end, there was no telling what was going on. For instance I hardly saw Richard once I'd stopped working on the residential unit, so when I finally managed to catch up with him, I was relieved to see that although he looked pale and tired, he was still his old robust self. I had heard that he had been off sick and naturally feared the worst, but he reassured me that nothing had been seriously wrong. Nevertheless, since the summer he had suffered from minor complaints such as shingles, herpes and gum disease, all of which had been enough to make him take stock. His faith in successful medical treatment had been tempered by time and he now accepted that he was on a road from where there was no turning off. The only unknown factor was how long the journey would take.

As far as I knew he was the only nurse on the unit who had openly declared his HIV status and he was determined to use this to good effect. With more and more residents learning of their diagnosis passively, in other words through the sudden onset of illness, the unit was having to deal increasingly with people who were in turmoil and he wanted to be used within this framework by staff and residents alike. He had noticed, however, that colleagues often appeared reluctant to approach him and he wondered if he was experiencing an element of staff denial.

Richard had previously spoken to me of his own denial, but it seemed that anyone who worked on the unit, and who openly acknowledged their status, was surely facing their future head-on. 'I try to look at it as close as I can and not to be too blinkered,' he told me. 'I read things on the subject and I watch documentaries about AIDS but also I know when to turn things off or when to video something and watch it another time.'

I knew that there were times when working on the unit became an unbearable strain for him. He told me that the experience of looking after one particular resident, who had recently died and to whom he felt he had been unable to offer any comfort, had left him feeling vulnerable and distressed.

'He had the worst KS I have ever seen and I listened to his discomfort and to his words of pain and I felt totally useless. He was hitting back at his nurses and accusing us of not ending his life for him. He would have taken anything to be rid of the world. On one level I was relating to him as a human being, but on another level I was thinking "what the hell do I do if this happens to me?" In the end I had to block it out because you can't live your life imagining the worst all the time. I couldn't continue working if I lost the ability to block certain things out. In that respect, I think some denial is healthy. Of course, occasionally I catch myself looking to see if there are any signs of KS on my body but I can't imagine my limbs ever getting as bad as his were. Presumably he felt just like me three years ago.'

Richard and his partner, who also worked at Lighthouse and had HIV, were an exemplary pair – considerate to others and devoted to each other. In their forties they were having to face what most couples don't have to face for another thirty years, in other words the knowledge that one of them would probably soon get ill and die. Richard had an idealised picture of the two of them deteriorating at the same rate, sharing the unit's only double room, and finally dying in each other's arms. 'The idea of dying before my partner is very painful to me,' he said, 'because I know how much it would distress him and drag him down.'

Richard was lucky to have a partner. Many people had never experienced this sort of love and mutual support and it was not unusual for people with HIV to be abandoned by their partners either after diagnosis or at the onset of illness.

Sadly, in the spring of 1992 I learnt that Beatrice was one of these people. As the months had progressed I had seen progressively less of Beatrice, partly because I was not at Lighthouse nearly so much myself and partly because she'd moved to South East London which meant that coming to Ladbroke Grove required enormous effort. But then one day I bumped into her in Portobello Road and we stopped to have a coffee in a nearby cafe. I was sorry but not surprised to learn that she had split up with her boyfriend.

'The strain was too great,' she told me. 'He thought he could handle it when I was still well but when I became ill we both realised that he couldn't. Living with someone who is terminally ill but asymptomatic is a totally different ball game to living with someone who is chronically ill all the time. I remember when I was first diagnosed he professed to being this large, lovable, broad-minded man who could cope with any calamity but in actual fact when it came down to it he was just a big coward and ran out on me when I needed him most.'

Beatrice didn't seem unduly bitter about having been deserted precisely at a time when the disease was taking a strangle hold of her life, but she wished he could have gone and done it earlier when it would have been easier to adjust to living alone. In a way, she felt her life was simplified by not having a relationship and it made her better able to concentrate on her own desires and needs.

She had seen her daughter, Chloe, twice in the past five months. Once in London and once in Ireland – both had been happy, fruitful meetings and she seemed less trau-matised by the separation. But I was sad to see that she was in a pretty bad state of health. The thrush in her mouth was so severe that she could hardly swallow and she was walking with a great deal of difficulty. A more optimistic sign, however, was that her dementia did not appear to have advanced. It now seemed likely, she told me, that she hadn't been suffering from dementia at all but rather from the effects of certain drugs which were causing some kind of temporary cognitive impairment.

When we parted company she gave me her telephone number and I promised to ring her in a few weeks time as I was about to go away on holiday. She lived in Lewisham and although she had good support from her social services department, most of her friends lived north of the river and I had the feeling that she felt very isolated down there, cut off from the people and places that mattered most.

As promised I phoned her at the beginning of May on my return from holiday but was surprised to hear a man's voice on the other end of the phone. 'Can I speak to Beatrice?' I asked and waited for her to pick up the receiver. But instead there was a silence and, after some hesitation, the man asked me who I was. I told him my name without any explanation of how I knew Beatrice as for all I knew he might have been unaware of the true nature of Beatrice's illness. After another pause, the man then said – this time in a softer voice – 'I'm sorry to have to tell you, love, but Beatrice passed away ten days ago.'

I was stunned. Although logic and experience should have told me that the last time I'd seen Beatrice she was extremely ill and probably wouldn't survive the summer, it seemed so terribly sudden. I told the man I was extremely sorry to hear the news but did not ask for any details concerning the manner and cause of her death. I had a feeling it was Beatrice's father on the other end, who was her only living relative, and would no doubt have come to London to arrange the funeral and sort out her belongings. She'd always described him as a warm and generous man and I was not in the least bit surprised since his main concern during our brief conversation seemed to be to make sure that I wasn't too upset at having had the news broken to me in such an abrupt and impersonal manner.

The news of Beatrice's death shocked me, and I was particularly sorry not to have said goodbye to her. Although I did not believe that death with HIV was inevitable, sometimes it certainly seemed that way. People may have rallied, got better and done things they'd never dreamt of doing, but almost always the advances and retreats of the disease were just a part of a relentless cycle which all too often culminated in death.

Because of this cycle, London Lighthouse was an extremely stressful place to work and the potential for burn-out was of course enormous. One group head told me that she had seen it happen on a number of occasions and it often manifested itself by someone suddenly being unable to feel anything when a service user died. A member of the management team who had worked at Lighthouse since 1987 and left shortly after I started working there told me one of the reasons why he was going: 'I'm burnt out on the issue, which is something that happens to a lot of social workers. It means you start getting resentful of people using the services, you start working to rule, you're permanently exhausted from lack of sleep and you have no enthusiasm for the subject anymore. Also, the climate of negativity around the issue of AIDS is so great that people direct it at organisations like Lighthouse and I'm afraid I have found it increasingly difficult to be involved in creative work when it is constantly being pilloried.

'On another level, I can no longer cope with people deteriorating in front of my eyes and so I shut off from all that. I have never been able to deal with it well because I have a tendency to avoid the issues surrounding loss and bereavement. My nature is to work hard and get on with things, and unfortunately at Lighthouse I haven't been able, or prepared, to break through that conditioning.'

For volunteers burn-out was not usually such a problem for the obvious reason that we were not saturated with the issue from morning till night. As far as I was concerned only occasionally did I feel I'd had enough and this was usually because I'd taken on more than I could deal with. When Kim came to Lighthouse for palliative care, I would visit him every few days, sometimes sitting with him for two hours or more as he drifted in and out of sleep. When he spoke he made no sense and no one was sure whether his confusion was a result of dementia or the drugs he was on. As I sat by his bedside I experienced for the first time how visitors to the residential unit were sustained and nourished by the warmth and welcome they received there: watching Kim's rapid deterioration was a sad and depressing business but how much worse it would have been had he been admitted to one of the large London hospitals.

All the same, at that time I would leave Lighthouse longing for the impersonal normality of the streets below, relieved to get away from the residential unit, the atmosphere of which was at times so intense as to make my head reel, making me feel disorientated and claustrophobic.

But this intensity was at the same time what made Lighthouse such a unique and rewarding place to work in as it allowed strong relationships to develop between those who used the services and those who provided them. This was a particularly precious aspect of life at Lighthouse, offering involved support and affection on a personal level and on a professional level providing a continuity of care which was hard to match in the statutory sector. However, the other side of this closeness was the degree of loss and grief felt when someone died.

Loss at Lighthouse was not only experienced when people with AIDS died but also when staff and volunteers left due to burn-out or managerial upheaval. This had been a key element in the initial structuring of the organisation and had been cause for concern ever since.

In the 1989 London Lighthouse annual report Christopher Spence wrote: 'All change involves loss, and as the rise in the number of people affected by AIDS continues on a steep upward curve, the organisational changes required for an effective response to be maintained are accompanied inevitably by mounting personal losses. At Lighthouse we struggle painfully with managing as well as we possibly can essential and frequent organisational upheaval, and increasingly, the many losses that follow.'

I did not doubt the sincerity of these sentiments. Christopher Spence was a man of vision, of passion and of considerable perception and if these remarks seemed sometimes to fall on deaf ears, or were more effective in word than they were in deed, it was only because many of his ideas were too radical to be easily and quickly assimilated into the organisation. I felt it was bound to take years, and in the growing process would inevitably lead to more upheaval.

The ambiguities which operated within London Lighthouse were sometimes glaring. Indeed, one of the things Christopher Spence had tried to develop was an understanding that everyone was engaged in the process of managing ambiguity, loss and change; and that ambiguity was to be welcomed, understood, come to terms with, managed creatively and not feared or taken to be some sign of failure.

In 1986 Christopher Spence wrote: 'Leadership is in the

first place about being human rather than about having a lot of people to lead. Therefore meeting the challenge of making our lives right now the best expression of what it means to be human is an important act of leadership.' Those people who felt disappointed with the direction that Lighthouse had taken and believed that it had never begun to implement, let alone fulfil, the aims set out in the vision statement, thought that Spence had fallen far short of creating a caring, non-judgmental style of management. While many still admired and respected him, there were also those who felt let down by him, believing he had, like many great reformers and idealists before him, lost touch with the people.

I sensed an unease among employees, both because some believed him to be a leader who wouldn't tolerate dissent, but also because funding was becoming increasingly precarious and Lighthouse's survival was no longer as secure as it once had been.

Spence was well trained in dealing with attack. The very fact that London Lighthouse existed at all, when powerful individuals and whole communities were opposed to it, demonstrated his tenacity in the face of criticism. As a result of attacks in the media he believed that great strength and unity had been found with Lighthouse and that such attacks were to be expected within the turbulent world of AIDS, especially in an organisation taking leadership on the issue. In an article written for *Lighthouse News* in March 1991, he wrote: 'AIDS touches too many raw nerves and frightens people. Fear stops us thinking and makes us feel bad, creates conditions in which it is often a little easier to criticise, blame and attack than to face our fear and take steps to find whatever help we need in order to begin thinking again.'

Some people held the somewhat narrow view that to

have an inspirational leader figure was by definition incompatible with the radical aims set out by London Lighthouse, namely to empower people affected by HIV and AIDS, even though it was Spence himself who created the spirit of staff consultation in order to protect and promote people's rights to autonomy in their work.

When I first joined Lighthouse, Spence appeared to me to be one of those impenetrable individuals who seldom, if ever, suffered from a crisis of confidence. He came across as someone utterly convinced that whatever he had to do was justified and that if he met with hostility along the way then that was only par for the course. But, as time went by, I soon realised that, like others, my feelings towards him were sometimes misguided and biased. Because of his inspiring presence and because he seemed always so firm in his resolve, I made assumptions about him which simply weren't true.

In fact I soon discovered that, like most people in an exposed leadership role, he suffered from doubts, fears and crises of confidence. As part of doing a difficult job as well as he could, he did not necessarily wear these feelings on his sleeve but anyone who chose to investigate soon learned the truth, including the fact that he consulted widely on whatever step he was taking – with management, with unions, with professional advisers, with staff members formally and informally, with funders, with other AIDS organisations and with members of the Council of Management to whom he reported managerially.

The toughest thing of all about working at London Lighthouse was having to let go of it after eighteen months of being a volunteer there. When I became pregnant with my second child and ended up in hospital for two months, I realised I could no longer commit myself on either an emotional or practical level. Life within its walls had anyway changed since I first stepped through the doors in January 1991. There were now new volunteers and staff and a whole set of new service users whom I would probably never have a chance of getting to know despite being determined not to break my ties with Lighthouse altogether.

On first encountering London Lighthouse some people (staff, volunteers and service users alike) – would find themselves sucked into its life so completely that it easily became their second home, and sometimes even their first. I had seen this happen on many occasions and had also watched how people eventually resurfaced the other side with the intention of re-establishing a life outside. I always sensed a danger in getting too dependent on Lighthouse and ultimately being let down by it.

At the beginning of my time as a volunteer I had fallen in love with the fantasy of Lighthouse, and as a result when I discovered that not everyone there loved or even liked each other, and that over the course of its five-year existence some people had been pretty harshly treated, for a while I felt saddened and disillusioned. In my naïvety I had hoped that AIDS could be this great leveller, allowing people to trust and respect each other again, but experience taught me that despite all the laudible goals of Lighthouse, some things weren't so easily attainable.

With a little more insight I came to understand that creating a philosophy was easy compared to the efforts it took to putting that philosophy into practice. As history has shown such endeavours take years to bear fruit and are fraught with obstacles along the way. The realisation of the ideals set out in London Lighthouse's vision statement was not yet possible, with the organisation being still so young and with AIDS touching on so many emotive issues. Also, since people at Lighthouse were encouraged to voice their opinions and to be open and honest, it was hardly surprising that ruptures sometimes appeared in the framework.

Nevertheless, despite having the same sort of managerial problems as any other establishment, London Lighthouse was no ordinary organisation and a lot of people like me found themselves profoundly affected by the place. I certainly felt changed and humbled by my experience there. In my life outside I found myself spending less time on superficial relationships, I felt more able to challenge prejudice, and generally I felt a little braver. With time in short supply and emotion always so near to the surface, I felt I was able to get close to people at Lighthouse in a way that I had never experienced before. Talking about the normally taboo subjects of sex, sexuality and death had, after all, been on the agenda from day one.

What I regretted most after leaving Lighthouse was no longer being able to inhabit this raw and passionate world which was so much more substantial than the one which existed outside. Life was richer at London Lighthouse because life was rarer and therefore a great deal more precious.